M

0

<

THE ENVELOPE

*A Study of the Impact of the
World upon the Child*

LONDON
GEOFFREY CUMBERLEGE
OXFORD UNIVERSITY PRESS

The ENVELOPE

A Study of the Impact of the
World upon the Child

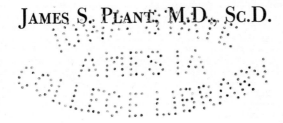

JAMES S. PLANT, M.D., Sc.D.

NEW YORK · 1950

THE COMMONWEALTH FUND

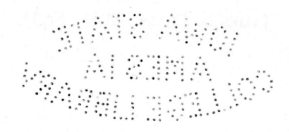

PUBLISHED BY THE COMMONWEALTH FUND
41 EAST 57TH STREET, NEW YORK 22, N.Y.

————

PRINTED IN THE UNITED STATES OF AMERICA
BY THE HILDRETH PRESS, INC.

Publisher's Foreword

DR. PLANT died on September 7, 1947. He knew before he died that this book, which had been long in the making, would be published by the Commonwealth Fund, but there had not been time for the editorial give and take which might have elicited his final thinking on the manuscript. Dr. Plant's preface to his earlier book, *Personality and the Cultural Pattern*, must therefore stand as his own comment on both volumes. As he said there, "If the book raises many questions and answers none . . . it is only a true picture of the years of work with those who look out upon life."

Dr. Plant was director of the Essex County Juvenile Clinic in Newark, New Jersey, for his last twenty-four years, and what he wrote came straight from that broad and rich experience. Those who knew his work best were impressed with his dual interest in it: his strong clinical feeling for the child, and his passion to learn what lay beneath the child's manifest difficulties. The combination of warmth and restless curiosity is evident in his books. This one in particular represents a struggle to bring together into an intellectually satisfying pattern his intuitions about the child and his sense of constantly shifting environmental pressures. But he could never be satisfied with a purely intellectual schematization, and so he gave the book its somewhat surprising title—as if to keep constantly before the reader that "non-logical" mechanism by which the child's personality comes to terms with the hard facts of the world which surrounds him. The facts could be classified; the child remained fluid and unique.

December, 1949

Acknowledgments

LIKE its predecessor, *Personality and the Cultural Pattern,* this book is an outgrowth and expansion of an outline prepared as my part of a Seminar in Personality Development assembled by the General Education Board at Hanover, New Hampshire, during the summer of 1935. It would therefore be incomplete without an expression of my debt to the organizer of the enterprise, Lawrence K. Frank, and the other members of that group. I am but one of a large number who owe a great deal to Mr. Frank's keen insights into the importance of a growing understanding of the no man's land between the biological and social sciences.

Once more, acknowledgment is due to the friends and counsellors who, as Chosen Freeholders of the County of Essex, New Jersey, have made possible the work at the juvenile clinic in Newark, and to those thousands of patients, without whose assistance the whole matter would have been impossible. They have fashioned the structure—and put in the mortar. The edifice which life itself builds often appears grotesque—but it is solid and well withstands the drives of better-ordered theory.

As in the case of the earlier book, I have gone over all the material of this volume many times in discussion with various groups and individuals, and I gladly acknowledge their help— and patience. A long list of names comes trooping—all have been of great assistance. Two demand specification: Professor Robert S. Lynd has patiently and wisely dealt with a good many of the immaturities of meaning and organization, and, my secretary, Miss Minnie Peckler, has been so conscientious and patient through the writing of both volumes, that it would be utterly unfair not to record my deep thanks here.

July, 1947   J.S.P.

Contents

Contents (continued)

Introduction

In dealing with people one is forever haunted by the question of how much each individual brings to a given situation —how much his inherent needs for growth predetermine the shifting, kaleidoscopic scenes in which he is involved. In a sense it is the only question that a person dealing primarily with people ever asks, and the social scientist needs the answer before he can go very far in his field. This book, which consists chiefly of raw material collected in working with ten thousand or so children, won't supply the answer, but the author hopes it will lead to further questions and new formulations.

The usual approach to this subject has been that of looking for certain recurring patterns in the mental life or behavior of a great number of individuals. The larger the sample and the wider its variety in age, economic and social status, ethnic background, and problems to be met, the more sure one would be that these distilled, recurrent residues represent characteristics of living tissue in making social adjustments. I am therefore sorry that my material comes only from children—and from those of a circumscribed area colored chiefly by the pigments of industrial and commercial America.

THE SOCIAL PRESSURES

Psychobiological and psychosomatic are on everyone's lips— psychosocial should be. For twenty years I have been sure that social pressures and trends are as important to the individual as the heart and the stomach, and I have hoped that the vital needs of the patient would shame us all out of our sectarian bickerings and misunderstandings. In the following pages, I have therefore included a great many references to data outside the usually

accepted psychiatric limit. A thoroughly competent sociologist
or educator could probably add a great many more, but as I am
interested less in exhaustive analysis than in opening vistas, I
shall be content if I succeed in bringing the psychiatrist to the
realization that the patient is an integral part of his environment.

In relying heavily on the Report of the President's Research
Committee on Social Trends,[1] I have chosen the most recent
authoritative survey of the whole field—a work which is a condensation of many important monographs, one which itself refers the reader to an enormous amount of reliable data. During
this preliminary period, when an attempt is being made to break
down the barriers between the individual and the social sciences,
the existence of a particular social trend at any given moment is
less significant than the fact that the presence of social trends in
a given area affects the problems involved. In other words, when
a psychiatrist is considering the problem of security for a child,
it is important that he should know that there is a not-to-be-
denied trend towards more or fewer persons in each household
rather than exactly what the trend is in 1947. My notes therefore
tell him no more than where he can go to find the actual information.

THE ENVELOPE

Between the need of the child and the sweep of social pressures
lies a membrane—a sort of psycho-osmotic envelope of transcending importance, which gives its name to this volume.[2] One should
never think of this as a tangible, material structure. It is rather
a property of that part of the personality which is in touch with
the environment. If one must neurologize, then the envelope is
certainly to a large extent a cortical structure—at least its function and properties disappear in conditions (such as cortical
edema) that seem particularly to affect the cortex. Moreover, it

[1] *Recent Social Trends in the United States* (New York, McGraw-Hill, 1933).
[2] Plant, p. 232.

seems to grow in efficiency and complication as the individual grows from childhood—and this at least parallels the growing use of cortical structures.

For lack of a better shorthand term I have spoken of psycho-osmosis as occurring in this area. Normally the personality has the ability to shut out large sectors of its environment and to translate those parts that it takes in into usable or understandable material. It is the part of the personality where this selection occurs that I call the envelope. The word strongly suggests a covering, and confessedly I have little proof that the process operates on the periphery of the personality. Some of my anecdotal material, however, appears to be in favor of an outside location. Each of us sometimes has the experience of "not even hearing" or "not even seeing" unwanted material. Take, for example, a person lecturing to a group on problems of child-rearing (which, of course, assumes an intelligible lecturer and an alert and intelligent audience). If the members of the audience are requested to write out the lecture, the most amazing variants are discovered. Each of the listeners has "heard" a different lecture; each listener is possessed of a selective, osmotic membrane that allows him to hear only what he can afford to hear.

MEANING

It is only through the operation of the envelope that we can get at the problem of meaning—what anything "means" to the individual. The notion is by no means new. Freud and his followers have taken its existence so much for granted that they have said much less about it than its importance deserves. Certainly one of the most brilliant of the psychoanalytic contributions has been the theory that one sees the world only as he can afford to see it—that the material of the environment is sensed by the personality only in terms of the problems which it is trying to work through. Indeed it is apparent that the whole concept of

"meaning" as it is used in the present book is one that the psychoanalysts have long accepted as basic to their whole theory. In this
particular area of theory, however, I should disagree with them
in two respects. I assume that the personality has many "problems" instead of a few; also, that action and interaction produce
a constantly shifting rearrangement of the elements involved.
Psychoanalytic theory postulates the personality as a beleaguered
defender who wins or loses on the basis of the extent to which
his plan of action can fend off the enemy.[3] My concept is rather
that while the defender has certain fairly persistent goals in mind,
these are constantly being reconsidered—the day-by-day stand
changed on the basis of yesterday's victory or defeat. I place the
envelope wherever the defender is in contact (or expects to be
in contact) with the attacker. Thus the areas protected by the
envelope—and the implications of the envelope—are constantly
changing. To the rear lie bases of supplies, plans of attack, re-
serves, and so forth. Though the following chapters represent
merely an effort at guessing what is in the territory behind (or
inside) the envelope, I feel sure that this is the only way in which
those "total resources of each army" can be understood.[4] So far
we know very little about the envelope; when we know more
about it we shall have our best approach to the study of the total
personality.

THE PROBLEMS

A great deal has been written in attempt at analysis of the personality, in picturing its inner structure. The present volume is
concerned less directly with its structure than with its activity in
trying to solve certain problems. This is not to escape the important matter of describing the personality, but to approach it in a
dynamic way.

[3] The conflict concerning the "incestuous" nature of the early object-love. Healy,
p. 105.
[4] Plant, Chapter III, particularly pp. 54 ff.

The reader will, with me, feel a certain unevenness in the values of the twenty-one problems detailed in the following chapters. Some will seem the results of a working out of the others; some will seem to belong to tissue growth; some probably depend much more on the exigencies of the cultural pattern. I am in no sense ready to build the sort of hierarchy that this demands—and warn against its being tried at this time. My tentative feeling is that interplaying tensions are of such extreme variety and complexity that the problems should not be schematized until we are more sure of their foundation. If we could, in these next years, come to recognize a certain number of recurring patterns in growth, and if we could see what this implies in our total construct of the personality in a cultural pattern—that would be enough for now.

Other authorities have made similar lists—one with a single problem,[5] one with as many as forty-four, and there is every sort of scatter between these. The number is not important; it pretty largely depends upon the personality of the one who makes the study. He who is objective in his thinking finds many; he who is ready with generalities and symbols nimbly develops relationships and can see them all as one. The method is important—that we carve out of each total situation those needs or problems which must be reckoned with for each child each time we see him. In describing twenty-one of these, I have consciously run beyond a practicable formulation, believing that in the end it would be easier to combine certain problems than to tease them apart and that less distortion would be involved.

None of these twenty-one problems is ever really solved. In the matter of security, for example, adjustment is not so much a matter of attainment as of acceptance of the fact that one is always looking for it. So in the following chapters I have listed the ways

[5] "All other conclusions of psycho-analytical theory are grouped around [the Oedipus] complex and by the truth of this finding psycho-analysis stands or falls."
—Ernest Jones, quoted in Healy, p. 13.

in which each problem is formulated and, for each of these ways, there is a chronological outline of critical curves and changes in direction (inflection points). I hesitated a long time before putting in these dates. However, it seemed to me that if this book is to be of the slightest use to persons actually handling children they ought to be told about when one looks for this or that development, about how far it is to the next corner.

Furthermore, I am not sure that every child at every moment is engaged in all twenty-one areas. Sometimes, indeed, a youngster seems so preoccupied with the difficulties of one problem that all the others are forgotten. Sometimes he seems so comfortable in working out one problem as to be cheerfully unaware of what we can see to be a wretched state of affairs in many of the others. But when we say, "We see children who . . .," we mean to include a large percentage of those we have seen (and we suspect that we include all).

CHAPTER 1

Security

We see children who sense that they have a position in life which is unassailable because of who they are, and which cannot be assailed regardless of what they are or do; and we see others who search and strive constantly for this. It is difficult to describe a person who feels that he "belongs"—this is some imbedded realization of being "a part of the scheme of things"—but it is a real phenomenon, even if so hard to describe. Its wholeness encompasses the entire personality, endowing it with a certain sure-footedness.[1]

The essential factor in the issue of security is its unreasonable-ness—its defiance of rational analysis. The child's place in his own family is not determined by anything that he is or does. That the family sometimes fails to recognize his claim does not deny the fact that, to the child himself, here is a set of relationships which no amount of conduct can erase. Their degree of pleasantness or unpleasantness may change, but not their existence. If, on this basis, we recognize that the accident of birth is the determining factor, we confidently expect the same issues in the child's early reactions to his racial problems.[2]

The fact that I use "security" rather than the more popular "belongingness"[3] is not so important as the fact that in my formu-

1 An excellent discussion of these pictures is given by A. H. Maslow, "The Dynamics of Psychological Security-Insecurity," *Character and Personality*, vol. x, no. 4, pp. 331–344, June 1942. The physician is always in difficulty here because he deals so much with illness that he finds himself thinking of health—or any positive situation —as merely the absence of negative or disturbing symptoms.

2 Chapter 13.

3 For an extended discussion of this whole problem, see Plant, in many places but particularly pp. 95–109. See also Chapter 2 of the present volume, where a distinction is made between the belongingness and authority aspects of security.

lation the term denotes something quite different from "adequacy."[4] In this area my classification has been increasingly based upon the way in which children react to given sets of experiences.[5] As I came to recognize that the insecurity was expressed in terms of anxious, panicky behavior (rather than in the fear and overcompensation typical of inadequacy), I began to separate the experiences which affect children in the two situations. Because the distinction has been generally overlooked,[6] the insecure child is still dosed heavily with scholastic success, acclaim in competitive sports, new sleds, and other such trickery—all of which does well enough for problems of inadequacy.

At this point I should like to reaffirm my belief in the hopelessness of providing security through outside, "mechanical" means. Psychiatrists who recognize that one cannot replace a lost arm or materially change a low I.Q. will do well to accept in similar fashion that security or belongingness cannot be ladled out to the child. I have thought that insecure children might find belongingness in their religious life ("God cares for me just because I am a person, one of His children"), but I have actually had only a handful of cases where this seems to have occurred—though perhaps the explanation may be that the children who come to the clinic are not over sixteen. Also, I have supposed that these insecure youngsters might get complete belongingness in their own married life—from spouse or children. But I don't really know whether they do. However, I see a great many insecure parents—and have to answer the question with the reminder that if security had been attained, I should tend not to see them.

This volume will give the impression of disagreeing with the

[4] Chapter 14.

[5] Kurt Goldstein has set up about the same dichotomy, coming at the whole question from an entirely different angle. See, *Human Nature in the Light of Psychopathology* (Cambridge, Harvard University Press, 1940), pp. 85–119.

[6] One exception appears in D. M. Levy's recognition of the difference—he using the term "primary affect hunger" for my "insecurity." See, "Primary Affect Hunger," *American Journal of Psychiatry*, vol. 94, no. 3, pp. 643–652, November 1937.

earlier book, in its picture of the quest for security as a continuing one. There the reader is rather invited to feel that once the individual has attained belongingness, it is irrevocably his.[7] The reason for this is that the issue of security is perhaps the first to be met, so that fairly soon narrower swings of adjustment obtain for new questions as they arise in this area. Thus adjustment becomes an habitual attitude even though the quest goes on, in a relatively circumscribed area.

A question corollary to that of the previous paragraph is whether the child who finds security in his relationship with his parents, can ever really lose it. In other words, is it a part of the unreasonableness of belongingness that, once attained, it can never completely disappear? The answer is clouded by two considerations. Where we see insecure children and where we get a "history" of earlier security, it is very easy and very tempting to say that the child merely *thought* he was secure in that earlier period. One is constantly amazed at how long and how quietly a "problem" can remain out of awareness if the rituals of life (being passably good-looking, having passable intelligence, manners, and, for one's group, material goods) are colorlessly fulfilled. The second difficulty is more complicated. The whole matter of security certainly stems in part from the fact that the only thing which cannot be taken from a person is his parentage.

For a great many of our patients it is the orientation that parents give, rather than the love that they give, that means security. The child's parentage still tells him who he is, still gives him certain bearings for the voyage of life—even if these same parents hate each bit of his flesh. In this sense security is irrevocable— and must be accepted as such (because it is so definitely a reality to many of our patients) even if the condition has very little to do with our usual definition of the word. However, where security means that the child is cared for because of who he is, not

[7] But see Plant, p. 90.

merely told who he is, there is considerable evidence that security
can be lost, even if once relatively completely attained. Part of
the evidence of this appears in the following pages, where we see
the search for security continuing through life. Part of it lies in
the clinical evidence of seeing anxious, panicky, loss-of-morale
types of reaction in children who are unquestionably secure in
their family relationships. On the other hand, we have known a
few children who gave no indication whatever of insecurity when
we first saw them and then developed typical and unquestionable
symptoms under our very eyes. This was not uncommon during
the depression. Some few families which we had known well before that time were hit so hard and so often by disaster that real
panic developed. This affected the children in similar fashion—
even where there had been a sound foundation of security earlier.

It is rarely the purpose of a book to complicate issues, but
sometimes life leads us in that direction. Therefore we must acknowledge the present large and growing use of the word "rejected" for children who are, or give the symptoms of being,
insecure. However, between the truly rejected and the merely
inadequate child, there is a third large group for which I use
the term "unwanted." (Obviously the specific name is of no importance so long as we recognize the symptom-complex and the
need of a convenient term for it.) As of the 1940's, about four out
of five children who are labeled "rejected" should really be
classed as "unwanted." Indeed, as I use the term, each of us has
been many times unwanted—very much so. The picture of anxious panic, of absorbing need for reassurance, of poor sportsman-
ship, of regressive behavior appears in both types of children—
but comes and goes with the unwanted child. Parental rejection
of the child appears in both pictures, but (in that of the unwanted
child) removal of financial stress or worry or fatigue or what not,
changes this parental attitude immediately. For instance, I have
often decided that a delinquent child was showing typical reac-

tions of insecurity—only to find him thoroughly secure a month later (when perhaps his father had a job, his mother was over an operation, and the neighborhood had calmed from the drama of the delinquency). As this is not a treatise on diagnosis or therapy, I pause here merely to say that one is wise to make the diagnosis of rejection (or insecurity) only in the presence of all four of the following pictures: (1) The catalogue of evils. This is the endless list of the wrong things the child does. Often a mother comes with them written down to be sure that she will forget none. Efforts at getting her to "list the good things" just don't succeed. (2) The rotten apple in the barrel. This child, the parent says, is now spoiling the others in the family. It wasn't so bad as long as there wasn't this unfair involvement of the ones who had been so nice. (3) It isn't as though the parents hadn't tried. They have always leaned over backward to give more to this child than to the others and to do more for him. (4) It's practically impossible to get the rejected child to leave home willingly. This is hard to understand, since he has such browbeating treatment there. It's as though he craved even the smallest crumbs of what he might get at home.

Unless the social engineer makes this distinction between the rejected and the unwanted child he will go on being amazed at the changing picture of insecurity in the child. In what is said in this and my earlier work as to insecurity I have always excluded unwanted children (where the severity of a particular family crisis gives a temporary picture of rejection). However, a rigorous adherence to not making the diagnosis of rejection except in the presence of the four pictures described above, keeps one from unnecessary trouble.

In these tempest-tossed days one cannot resist indicating the extent to which the issue of security is being fought out through Western civilization. Totalitarian forms of governance very possibly are going to succeed or fail precisely on this issue of whether the State or race can fully meet the problem of security.[8] It is no matter of chance that totalitarian groups attack the Family and the Church—their only real rivals in giving belongingness. The psychiatrist would have the temerity to say that if such totalitarian groups cannot satisfy this need, they will fall—regardless of military or economic success (on the assumption that our drift is towards an individual-centered culture, as explained in the earlier volume).[9]

In the very first weeks of life the child seeks answer to this problem in the cuddling psychomotor expressions of the mother. What we call the envelope[10] is a pretty inefficient affair at this time (if it has developed at all), so that the mother's real feelings towards this new event in her life sweep through the baby in all their harshness or their compelling richness. There are many interesting trends here, including those in bottle as opposed to breast feeding as well as those in the employment of married women.[11] The effect of the former is not easy to measure now, because so many pediatricians recognize the issues involved and therefore emphasize the great importance of cuddling and fondling bottle-fed babies. Of particular importance are trends in the social acceptance of pregnancy and its sequelae,[12] in how "proper" it is to have children.[13] When a child arrives in the Brown family there is little consideration there, or in the neighborhood, of the sweeps of pressure from changes in the cultural pattern (though the parents themselves are a part of those very pressures); psychiatrists are equally blind to what is happening if

[8] E.g., in Nazi Germany, Fascist Italy, and Soviet Russia there was an effort to give security to every individual who belonged to a certain racial stock or to a certain political organization.

[9] Plant, in many places, particularly pp. 237 f.

[10] See Introduction and Chapter 23.

[11] *Trends*, pp. 711 ff. Up to 1940 surprisingly few married women were employed, but the war saw a sharp increase in such employment as well as in the birth rate.

[12] *Trends*, p. 422.   [13] *Trends*, pp. 46–53.

they bank on years of personal contact between parents and children.

We psychiatrists have no data on insecure babies, though it is our theory that insecurity gets its start during these earliest days.[14] The pediatrician well knows the cranky, "upset" child of the mother who resents her new burdens. Possibly this is the syndrome of insecurity in the newborn (even if the pediatrician persists in placing the blame on the chemistry of the mother's milk!). Aldrich has gone even further, in describing infants who appear to be the analogue of the restless, anxious, panicky older child whom we term insecure.[15] The relationship between the two is not certain.

Almost at birth racial customs, pattern, and position also begin to play a rôle. The eldest son, for example, may be given "racial" security by virtue of his member rôle in the family,[16]

14 Plant, p. 21.

15 See C. A. and M. M. Aldrich, *Feeding Our Old-Fashioned Children* (New York, Macmillan, 1941), p. 39.

16 I find this a happy and useful term, but have had a great deal of difficulty in locating an authoritative definition. Robert S. Lynd writes me (1942):

"To the best of my knowledge this is one of the standard terms of the past fifteen or so years, especially in family research—e.g., 'family member rôles.' It is used to refer to the complex of overt behavior, attitudes, emotional responses imputed to one and learned by one as one grows up in a given familial or other membership position in a given group. Thus one would have a member rôle as a member of a biological family, another as a member of a neighborhood, another as a member of a club, school, church, etc.

"I suspect that one would not use the rôle concept in referring to so vague a thing as 'citizenship' in a very loosely organized social system like that of the United States; but one would use it with reference to the highly organized German social system under the Nazis. It seems to me useful wherever, by reason of social identification of a type of position in society, people expect things of an individual (not hit or miss expectations but fairly consistent ones). These expectations may be common to all social units of a given type—e.g. all families in our culture expect 'loyalty,' 'respect' (of sorts) by children for adult members, 'cooperation.' And the expectations of course take on special color and emphasis in special groups—i.e. Jewish families have special expectations of an intensive sort of their members, and some families have quite special degrees if not kinds of expectations of various members.

"In general the concept seems to me more useful as a general one—i.e. to family member rôles as patterned in a given culture or as patterned among Jewish families, etc.—rather than to refer to idiosyncratic rôles in peculiar individual families. Ad-

and correspondingly there is a threat to belongingness from having a less important member rôle. So far as the child's reaction is
concerned, we see the same "symptoms" as for the area involved
in the previous section. This is to be expected, since these racial
factors are transmitted to the child only through the persons of
the parents, who themselves often have the greatest difficulty in
separating personal feeling tones from those left by the sweeps of
racial dreams, goals, or patterns. Various trends play important
rôles here. First would be those in loss of "race consciousness" in
this country.[17] Next would be those in the dislocation of the usual
member rôle of the male[18] by serious economic depressions and
in the growing economic and social independence of women.[19]

There is a further series of trends which are hard to measure
but about which there is a growing amount of data. These have
to do with accepted beliefs that children in a certain position in
the family (e.g., the oldest or youngest child born in this country
of Old World parents) are particularly likely to be problem children.[20] Tied into this part of the problem is the issue of security
for any child of a minority race—a matter just touched on here,
as it is dealt with extensively in Chapter 13. As it will appear
there, the child is not directly confronted by this issue until his
third or fourth year, but indirectly he must meet it long before,
by contagion with his elders. At first he feels threatened, not because he belongs any the less in his own family but because he

mittedly the high drama is between the culturally patterned rôle expectation and
the very specific demands of *my* mother on *me* as her son.
  "Katharine Dupre Lumpkin's *The Family*, published by the University of North
Carolina Press (1933), is a study of family member rôles. It is one of the few studies
built directly around the 'family member rôle' concept."
    [17] *Trends*, pp. 591–600.   [18] Young, pp. 616 ff.
    [19] *Trends*, pp. 679, 734 ff. What, for instance, happens to penis envy—so impor-
tant to psychoanalytic theory—in a culture that is rapidly changing the relative importance and independence of the two sexes?
    [20] Young, pp. 383–384. Also N. E. Shoobs and George Goldberg, *Corrective
Treatment for Unadjusted Children* (New York, Harper, 1942), *passim* and particularly pp. 133–142.

finds himself in a situation which he "can't do anything about."
At this early time the picture is largely one of the child's bewilderment over the fact that his social status (the things he's allowed
to do, the names he's called, etc.) is affected by something completely beyond his control or making. As he grows older this goes
over into a pervasive feeling that everything that is done to him,
every attitude that is built about him is because of his race (e.g.,
"because I am a Jew"). At what age the one picture goes over to
the other I don't know. The trends of importance will be discussed in the proper chapter—here need only be considered those
in community attitudes about minority races and the extent to
which they are threatening majority groups.[21]

My theory is that once racial insecurity has been really experienced, it never disappears. But for two reasons I have put this on
probation. The first is that we have had little experience at the
clinic with children over sixteen. The second is that insecurity is
hard to discern in situations of success. The symptoms are best
observed in the child's behavior under the pressure of difficult
tasks, where he quickly shows anxiety, a desire to give up, panicky
fear of the situation. Still, the readiness with which these symptoms recur when the child is faced with frustration or obstacle
has given me confidence in the theory that insecurity never really
disappears—once felt.

At about the same age (that is, three or four) family ancestry
and tradition begin to play an important rôle in orienting the
child to "who" he is ("I am one of the X's"). This is more important in some areas than in others—as, for instance, in the South,
where family name still carries weight. However, there are many

---

[21] *Trends,* pp. 567–582, 593–594. After seventeen years of a turbulent stirring of
racial problems and hatreds this seems a very old-fashioned reference. In any more
recent year it would be hard to find an assay of dependable calmness or sure-footed
measurement.

local patterns stressing the importance of the family in the community (the mill owner's family, for instance).[22] Trends in our consciousness of these economic or social stratifications are important[23]—though after all it is the *feeling* of this rather than the stratification itself that is the important matter in the certainty the child has of having a place, a fixed position, regardless of how well or badly he behaves. While I am sure that this is an important aspect of the problem of security, I have really no data on it from Essex County. Perhaps there is no area in the country where there is less crystallization of a family's social or economic position. In the more rural part of the county we have had occasional glimpses of security or insecurity in children who belong to certain families—but this is rare with us.

Again, it is early in infancy that various members of the household add to or detract from the child's feeling of security. So we see grandparents or aunts or uncles as individuals giving or failing to give the child the feeling that he is cared for because of who he is. This turns out, in clinic practice, to be a two-edged sword—such extra members are a constant invitation to the child to modes of punishing his elders or of buying security through the way he behaves. So we see running away, stealing, enuresis, or other attention-getting devices, but these have the peculiar quality of being directed *against certain people*. That is, we find the child stealing only from his mother, or wetting the bed only on the nights that Aunt Mary is in charge, and so on. There are few more exciting trends than those in the number of relatives living in the household.[24] Apparently the decrease in the family is rap-

[22] R. S. Lynd and Helen Lynd, *Middletown in Transition* (New York, Harcourt, 1937), pp. 74 ff.
[23] Lynd, *op. cit.*, pp. 69–73. This "break in the ladder" of opportunity, so that there is increasing likelihood of one's remaining at the general social level of his parents, must slowly act towards telling each person "who" he is—in class as well as in family.
[24] *Trends*, pp. 681–683.

idly intensifying the emotional load on a very few people. The issues are clearer, the successes richer, the failures not to be escaped from.

The problem is complicated by the fact that there are certain hangers-on (more distant relatives, servants, *et al.*) who contribute, or fail to contribute, to the security of the child without being such an integral part of the household as this—for purposes of continuity and solidity—would imply. Consequently all trends as to the number of persons in the household should be broken down into the relationship of these persons to the child.[25]

Much that has been said about the household also applies to the extended family. However, as the clan disperses, all sorts of new avenues of contact are created which have security values for adults as well as children. These include various formal modes of communication and joint participation in ceremonies and celebrations. The influence upon those who are left is varied.[26] In some instances their value in giving security is depreciated because everyone (the child included) recognizes that he is part of a rapidly disintegrating affair. But in our experience those who are left more often find their security-giving value enhanced because they symbolically carry the load of the extended family. There is a corresponding difference in reaction when members of the extended family die or permanently leave the vicinity of the household. Sometimes the influence of such person diminishes quite rapidly, but quite as often his security value increases

[25] *Trends*, pp. 672–673.
[26] Statistical evidence of this well-recognized trend is extremely difficult to find. The reader should peruse the first two volumes of W. I. Thomas and Florian Znaniecki, *The Polish Peasant in Europe and America* (University of Chicago Press, 1918), and particularly vol. I, pp. 87–106. C. A. Ellwood's *Cultural Evolution* (New York, Century, 1927) gives the historical setting. W. Ogburn's chapter on "The Family" in *Trends* gives some data about the size of family groups within one domicile, but that of course is far from being the important point. Also, there is a considerable body of data of this last sort in Mildred Parten, "A Statistical Analysis of the Modern Family," *Annals of the American Academy of Political and Social Science*, vol. 160, pp. 32 ff., March 1932.

—the envelope no longer has to reinterpret his every act to make it mean that he is giving security. Now the child is completely free to say, "He would have forgiven me."

It is hard to tell just when the envelope begins to have to adjust the whole problem of belongingness to the fact that others also want to belong (part of the problem of sibling rivalry).[27] We know very well the point at which this part of the problem bursts into dramatic evidence—a bit previous to or just after the arrival of the next younger child. But, without question, in more subtle and less easily measured ways it presents itself before that. From its inception it is affected by the adequacy of the child[28]—his relative ability, accomplishment, attractiveness, and so forth. Children react in every conceivable way to threats in the area of sibling rivalry. But where, as here, it affects the child's feeling of security, there is a very general tendency for him to regress to infantile reactions (enuresis, soiling, thumb sucking, temper tantrums, etc.). The trends that stand out are: those in the size of the family,[29] those in the tendency to cluster children as to ages,[30] those in the tendency of the cultural pattern to favor any particular child (as the oldest), and changes in these.[31] Two other matters are important here though they cannot be considered as trends. One is brought out by the data relating to the variability in traits and attributes of siblings,[32] the other by the enormous amount of material that comes to the family in the form of cultural propaganda as to "what children must be"—for example, that girls should play with dolls, boys should be mischievous, the desirability of high I.Q.'s, and so on. These member rôle loads which children have to carry are much more closely allied to the

[27] Chapter 20.   [28] Chapter 14.
[29] *Trends*, pp. 683–686.   [30] Mildred Parten, *loc. cit.*
[31] Willystine Goodsell, "The American Family in the Nineteenth Century," *Annals of the American Academy of Political and Social Science*, vol. 160, p. 15, March 1932.
[32] *Trends*, p. 698.

adequacy than to the security problem, but at this point the two are pretty intimately interwoven. Regardless of one's theory it is extremely difficult to keep the child's security disentangled from his adequacy—or, for that matter, from his inadequacy. How often we see a tremendous security tie developed for the weak or the handicapped.[33]

When the child goes to school, at the age of five, or to nursery school considerably before that, the problem of security has to encompass the new "mother"—to compare what he gets from her with what he has had from his parents. Each thing that has gone before affects the relationship. If the child has had his fill of security, he may not even bother to look for it in the new situation or he may diligently seek an equally satisfying experience. If there has been insecurity in the home, the child may seek belongingness in full measure from the teacher—or, finding her of a mothering sort, may turn home with a not-to-be-denied demand for as much from his own people or with an equally disturbing punishment of them for what they have failed to give. Because these acute phases of comparison and weaning are so much a part of the security problem, the time at which this school adventure first occurs is of the greatest importance. This is less a matter of chronological age than of how far the problem has been worked through. Where the child is pushed out to school without sufficient security bases in the home, he tends to present regressive types of behavior—refuses to go to class, has temper tantrums, develops infantile speech or enuresis, and so forth. On the other hand, we sometimes see such children frantically reaching out towards the teacher for belongingness— hanging on her with pressing attention-getting devices. The trends here are varied. Most important, perhaps, are those in the

[33] Reinforced, often, by the feeling of guilt (see Chapter 4) which the parent has for having brought such a child into the world.

development of preschool ventures of which there are three distinct types.[34] Many are frankly parking places for young children;
others are just as frankly ventures in hurrying the emotional
growth of the child—snatching him as quickly as possible from
the dependence of the home. But there are a few nursery schools
which plan to involve the parent quite as much as the child—
helping the former to understand and to realize what problems
the child is trying to work through. It would seem obvious that
this last type of school can be safely turned to at any time; that the
second should not be imposed upon the child until he has had
his fill of security in the home (which in many families is given
even in the first few weeks of life); and that the first offers some
slight advantage at any age, since parents who merely wish a
parking place for a child would probably be poor companions for
him if forced to keep him at home.

There is another set of important trends that are much less
easy to see or measure. As the educators in this country have
gradually been developing a field wider than that of the three
R's, the school has reached out to replace a great many of the
family's traditional functions. In this scramble to pick the last
bits of flesh off the carcass, the school (along with other agencies)
has not realized that it cannot give belongingness. So there have
been distressing trends in the direction of failing to realize that
this important contribution must be made by the family and of
failing to realize that the child cannot comfortably face the problem of adequacy until he has made a fair adjustment to that of
security.[35]

Just as important as the child's preparation for school is the
character of person whom he finds to be his teacher. This raises
three important questions which the school is trying to solve:

[34] This is summarized in *White House Conference*, pp. 154 ff. See also *Trends*,
pp. 345, 788.
[35] Prescott, p. 203.

(1) To what extent is the child's academic progress affected by such emotional problems as that of belongingness? As educators have come to the realization that unsolved emotional problems play quite as serious havoc with the learning process as do diseased tonsils, they have tended to relieve academic pressure in the early grades. Obviously this affects but a small part of the total situation, but it is a noteworthy step forward. Here the trends in developing kindergartens and pre-kindergarten classes as a part of the public school system are important; and equally so are the trends in relieving the primary grades (kindergarten through third) of the load of academic curriculum.[36] Here also belongs the growing tendency to see the school years as life rather than merely a preparation for life.[37]

(2) What policy should be followed in regard to the training and selection of teachers? This emphasizes the importance of the present trends in training teachers for the problems of security they will face in these early grades;[38] and also that of the trend in selecting teachers who are sensitive to the emotional as well as the intellectual needs of people.[39]

(3) Are personality and background more important than high academic ability in teachers? This reflects interesting trends in stressing age, cultural background, and "security experiences" in the selection of persons to be employed as teachers.[40]

These questions indicate that a whole sector of the child's environment is becoming more sensitive to his emotional problems. But there is a second matter here—perhaps of equal importance—in the actual effect of certain of the teacher's problems upon the child. But important as this is, we know very little about it. However, we see examples of each of the following situations: The teacher's own insecurity sometimes spreads in

36 Prescott, pp. 206, 212 ff. 37 Prescott, pp. 197 ff.
38 Prescott, p. 203. 39 Prescott, pp. 277–278.
40 Prescott, pp. 263–264.

contagious fashion to her pupils, but it may also lead her to minister all the more wholeheartedly to their needs for security. The secure teacher, on the other hand, is sometimes so comfortably at ease that she is oblivious to the needs of others—a situation which may lead to apparently callous disregard of the insecurity of some rejected youngster. But just as frequently, in our experience, the teacher's security is assimilated by the whole group without the slightest awareness on her part of the fine job she is doing. Sometimes, also, this same happy security makes her peculiarly sensitive to the importance of a similar experience for the child. Thus either security or insecurity can lead the teacher (for different reasons, of course) to *have* to have the children's dependence—"I am a second mother to all the children."

This cataloguing of what a clinic sees in teacher-pupil relationships is put here in part as clinical evidence and in part to illustrate how complicated the various threads become the moment one leaves the question of what a teacher or a child does, to go to the more important one of what the teacher or child is *trying* to do—in terms of the envelope's translation of the progress of any one of these twenty-one different problems.

All through the childhood period (in differing years—depending on family circumstances) there is the security problem of the child in a broken family.[41] It will be simplest to state all three general principles involved here before mentioning the respective trends and the child's reaction to these. (1) The child's basic difficulty in the disappearance of one or both parents arises from the fact that his parent could care so little for him as to desert him. Thus a family broken by desertion represents a more distressing experience, in the child's eyes, than one broken by death.

[41] For a full discussion of this see J. S. Plant, "The Psychiatrist Views Children of Divorced Parents" in *Law and Contemporary Problems: Children of Divorced Parents* (Durham, Duke University School of Law, 1944), vol. 10, no. 5, pp. 807–818.

This distinction is of less importance in the very early years, since the child has not learned directly from his culture which kinds of broken families are "all right" and which aren't. (However, it must not be forgotten that the mother is acutely aware of the social implications of various ways of breaking families and that she spreads her security or insecurity by contagion to even a one-day-old infant.) (2) Step-parents can make children materially happy to the highest degree, but they do not answer the unreasonable belongingness needs of the child. (3) Parental discord frequently presents to the child all the real problems of not being wanted, of being rejected, that are present in actual desertion. Moreover, there is the increased irritation that comes from "forever having things stirred up." This means, often, that the actual step of divorce or desertion is a point of relief for the child.

The child's reaction to this situation is protean. If the envelope has not been able to protect him in any way from the starkness of the desertion, he comes to us as a beaten, anxious, panicky person; and, as if foreseeing this, the envelope makes the most valiant effort to interpret material in a way that is acceptable. Sometimes the child is told bizarre tales of the parent's death or of his long and exciting travels. If he can accept this much protection, he is able to fight back against warring parents or intruding step-parents—punishing them by all sorts of behavior disorders. (The situation is very different, though at first blush it may seem the same, from those in which the child makes up stories "of his own accord" to hide his confusion from his peers.) In the case of death, the child sometimes directs his resentment against the step-parent, feeling himself the surrogate of the dead parent; sometimes against the living parent, since he sees the latter as a deserter who has given his or her love to someone else.

There is a very high delinquency rate amongst children of broken families,[42] but we don't know how much of this results

[42] Young, pp. 629–631.

from emotional upset and poor supervision and how much from
the fact that the juvenile court and similar agencies are the most
available sources of therapy to which families of this sort can
turn. (If one has a fair income, delinquency so easily becomes a
conduct disorder—and is defined as a personality problem in our
best circles.) In many broken families dependency on public
relief intensifies the reactions just mentioned because it adds
the factor of lowered morale. This is true also where the problem
of neglect enters. I have long wondered how permanent the
results of dependency are, but I have not tried to make a study of
this and so have very little real data.[43]

The significant trends here are: those in the number of broken
families, classified as to desertion, divorce, or death—with the
ages and numbers of children involved;[44] those in the development of family courts and of clinics dealing with family problems, where we can assume that a start is being made in the
amelioration of difficulties in this area before they become too
serious;[45] those in the reassembling of families,[46] where the significant questions are how often and how soon people remarry,[47]
what happens to the children,[48] how permanent the reassembled
family groups are, and the social attitudes as to this.[49]

A separate section should be made for the search which some
children make for security in many informal situations and from
many persons carrying an informal or uncodified load (e.g., the

[43] During the early 1940's we saw many families—now doing very well financially
—who had been dependent for a long time during the depression. They said little
of the earlier years but tended to spend what they earned—a sort of "catching up"
process. How much of this is overcompensation for the earlier inferiority and how
much is the spirit of war times and inflation, I don't know.
[44] *Trends,* pp. 688–696. This is of course very rapidly increasing at the moment as
a postwar problem. But the long-time trend is definitely up, anyway.
[45] *Trends,* p. 1176.   [46] Young, p. 548.
[47] I. M. Rubinow, *Some Statistical Aspects of Marriage and Divorce* (American
Academy of Political and Social Science, Pamphlet Series, no. 3, 1936).
[48] Young, pp. 552–558.   [49] *Trends,* pp. 695, 1016.

village blacksmith). Each community has one or more persons who is mother or father to anyone who comes that way. The situation is much the same as that of the child's going to school,[50] except that here the youngster comes upon the person somewhat by chance while the school automatically provides such persons. In the general field of personality adjustment and delinquency the child seems to run away from insecurity rather than to seek security—that is, a great deal of the behavior arising in this problem is of a regressive sort towards a level that demands care and attention. In the matter under immediate discussion, however, there is often a rather active and persistent search for security. With some of our children, running away provides the mechanism—and in such instances the problem has been a stubborn one.

Trends in the "roaming range" of children are important—particularly those of broken as compared with unbroken homes.[51] We should like to know whether these security-dispensing adults flourish more in urban or in rural communities but have no data. Of course, at best they do not and cannot give full security in our sense of the word[52]—they do not orient the child as do his own parents (no matter what the degree of rejection). However, in their encircling acceptance of the child as such they do carry security loads, especially for insecure children.

In early years—perhaps by four—the child begins to hear and then to learn that the religious philosophy of the family or community contributes to his sense of belongingness—but now it is to the general scheme of things. He hears that God cares for him because of who he is and not fundamentally because of anything he has or anything that he has done. Until he is about seven such statements merely build up a framework for what

[50] See p. 19.   [51] *Trends,* pp. 176 ff.
[52] See pp. 9 f. for the two functions of the parents in giving security.

will later take on meaning for the individual in so far as the envelope allows. It would be interesting to know whether belongingness in the Church is sought earlier or more insistently by
children who are secure or those who are insecure in their own
families—but I have no data. The trends involved must include
those in family religious observances.[53] And they must include
church contacts with children through formal agencies, such as
Sunday school;[54] less formal agencies, such as Hebrew school and
vacation school; informal ties with organizations like the Boy
Scouts;[55] and propaganda which exerts indirect pressure on parents by means of slogans such as "The regular church-goer is not
a delinquent."

A great many children follow religious observances because
it is the thing to do—simply a pattern laid down for them. This
is not meant to argue against the reality of the experience, particularly as in the child's early years the entire experience is not
on a level involving religious meaning but rather "doing-what-I-
am-expected-to-do." It would be interesting to know the trends
in Sunday-school and church attendance for the children in different areas (as to the sorts of patterns that exert the most certain
pressure here), but unfortunately I lack data on these points.

From early adolescence on the Church gives a great many
children a sense of belongingness which has greater continuity
and certainty for the individual than anything provided by his
parents.[56] This is true whether the individual looks to a personal
God interested in him as one of His children, or finds in his religious experience an orientation to basic and everlasting
"values." There are two trends of importance. One is in the training of clergymen to realize the part the Church can have in

---

[53] E.g., in saying grace and family prayers (*Trends*, p. 674).

[54] *Trends*, p. 1034.

[55] *Trends*, pp. 1009, 1012, 1033, 1035 ff.

[56] This latter is most clearly set out in C. A. Wise, *Religion in Illness and Health*
(New York, Harper, 1942), particularly Chapter VII.

answering the child's need for belongingness.[57] The other is the Church's changing attitude in regard to its mission—towards a "moral and courageous attitude about social problems."[58] The outstanding periods of joining the Church are the two periods of crisis in sexual life (adolescence and the climacteric). To some extent this search for belongingness may be an indication of the at-sea-ness of the adolescent. As adolescence closes (this period runs rather beyond our clinic limits) there appear serious questions as to the strength and efficiency of the Church's claims. No delinquency is involved in this break with church observances, but the child frequently develops serious tensions from the fact that his culture constantly refuses to distinguish religious experiences from the formal symbols for these. Consequently he has a more difficult time in fitting his nonattendance at church with his natural need to feel that he is a "regular" part of his culture, than he has in questioning the formal claims of the church he has attended. Children tell me rather easily, "I am really deeply religious—it's only that I can't believe what *they* teach."[59]

In adolescence there is frequently a feeling of strangeness, of ill-at-ease-ness, similar to that of insecurity. (This is part of "how it feels to be an adolescent.") We know that this is a period in which the indices of maladjustment, delinquency and psychoses, take a sudden upward jump.[60] While it is probable that this is due to a considerable extent to biological factors, we must not forget that at this time our cultural pattern primarily asks the child what he can do—that there is a high premium put on adequacy.[61] There are family attitudes against cuddling, kissing by parents—"still acting like a baby." There is a definite tendency

[57] *Trends*, p. 1033.

[58] *Trends*, p. 1014. The Church militant finds it hard to give much time to the security needs of its members.

[59] There is a good discussion of this in Peter Blos, *The Adolescent Personality* (New York, Appleton-Century, 1941), pp. 296–298.

[60] *Trends*, p. 1137.   [61] Chapter 14.

towards determining the child's social position through competition.[62] Moreover, the various rites signifying "coming of age" stress the child's individual strength and dependence upon himself—rather than his security needs.[63] In other words, the issues involved here do not seem to be those of security-insecurity.[64] The "symptoms" are much less deep-seated, and they pass as the period of adolescence closes.

[62] Young, pp. 436–437.   [63] Young, pp. 408 ff.

[64] I am indebted to Professor Coyle of Western Reserve University for the hunch that this may be an incorrect statement. She points out that in many of the gangs (and other such groups) of this adolescent period there is an acceptance of the individual in spite of what he does. This may be a sort of substitute for the earlier security. I don't know much about it—but confess that I had been so dazzled by the fact that it is some show of adequacy that gets the child into the group, as to be blind to the possibility that there are real security values for him—once in.

CHAPTER 2

Authority

We see children who have to adjust themselves to the fact that they live in a world which can make them do things whether they wish to or not.[1] The problem appears for them at four levels: the authority of the body, the authority of parents and other older persons through possession, belongingness, and age; extra-human authority; and the authority of society. One never solves the problem of authority, though it is met early in life and each of us habituates himself in childhood to a certain attitude about it. We develop a sort of *modus vivendi*—a decision to "fight it out on these lines"—but the struggle does not cease. Thus, if by eight I have become the ritualistic slave of my alimentary demands, at seventy I am still trying, in much the same way, to answer these same orders.

In most instances, however, it is the possibility of control rather than the actual control that matters. One example will do. There is the disturbance which the child makes over his parents' plans to go out for the evening. Whether the issue is decided by their staying at home to quiet him, or the other way, he calms down and is soon asleep. That is, he is not disturbed over the fact of the parents' going out (for he evinces little interest in them if they remain at home) but over the fact that they can go out. It is to this possibility of control that each of us must adjust—and

---

[1] This is what I term "authority" (Plant, pp. 85–88) in distinction to "discipline." There is an excellent discussion of the subject in Ruth L. Munroe, *Teaching the Individual* (Sarah Lawrence College Publications, No. 3, Columbia University Press, 1942), Chapter III, where the corresponding terms are "discipline" and "coercion."

anyone who, in the name of individual freedom and growth, disregards it is unrealistic.

The problem of authority is first met at the physical level, and there is—throughout life—something akin to resentment against the authority of the body.[2] Perhaps this starts with the birth process—certainly there has been built a complete theoretical formulation of the problems of adjustment as ramifications of the importance of the trauma of birth.[3] We are therefore interested in trends in the number and seriousness of birth injuries.[4]

Then, during the first few years—beginning at about two or two and a half—some children are baffled by their failure to develop the reflexes of prehension and speech in accordance with their parents' expectations. Though our environment is geared to expect speech and coordination of hands and feet at certain ages, marked individual differences in the maturation of the nerves developing these reflexes occur as perfectly normal phenomena. Therefore, we are interested in trends in general knowledge as to "what children should be able to do" at certain ages.[5] These trends affect the child in three different areas. (1) First there is the standardization of preschool and kindergarten levels of demand and achievement.[6] (2) Then there is the series of trends growing out of the popularization of Madame Montessori's respect for the child's ability to judge his own readiness for

[2] Everyone—and particularly the devotees of psychobiology—will shudder at the separation of the physique from the personality, as is done in this section. My various organs indeed make up my personality (just as my house, my parents, and my street do), but in actual living they don't seem to—and it is in this spirit of realism that the following section is written.

[3] Otto Rank, *Trauma of Birth* (New York, Harcourt, 1929).

[4] E. A. Doll, W. M. Phelps, and R. T. Melcher, *Mental Deficiency due to Birth Injuries* (New York, Macmillan, 1932), pp. 2–11. If the process of birth is traumatic for the normal child, it must be still more so for one who has suffered even a slight injury.

[5] For a thorough discussion of this, see White House Conference (Section I, Committee A), *Growth and Development of the Child*. New York, Century [1932–1933].

[6] A. L. Gesell and others, *The First Five Years of Life* (New York, Harper, 1940).

these experiences. (3) And there are trends in experiments with toys—involving knowledge about fitting them into the child's own development or using them to influence what we want that development to be.[7] Where the child's coordinations do not develop as rapidly as his parents wish, one gets a tense, tied-up muscular picture—sometimes including irritability, restlessness, poor sleep. On the other hand, if the maturation of the nerves proceeds too rapidly, the child may break or pull apart toys—earning a reputation of being destructive.

It's the same in the area of speech—where, once more, we are considering the authority of a physical development as it controls the response of the child to his environment. We live in a culture which demands that its most important communications be expressed in words, so that there is anxious expectancy in regard to the child's talking, as this is looked upon as a measure of his success in the world in which he is to live. These trends have been reinforced by the great extent to which tests of "intelligence,"[8] even for these very tender years, are tests of the ability to verbalize. Because disturbances in speech are an accurate measure of emotional disturbance, children respond to their inability to meet these cultural demands with spastic and spasmodic forms of speech.[9] To add to the difficulty, these phenomena are self-perpetuating. If a child is upset, he shows it by stuttering (we even "stammer our thanks"), which makes him more upset. This in turn develops more tension in the adults about him, which leads to more stuttering, and so on. We have long known that, of all the children who stammer, only about one-twentieth do so as adults. Most of the cures are effected spontaneously, without benefit of psychiatric ministration. Part of the reason for this may be that as the child leaves the age of six or seven behind there

[7] Ethel Kawin, *The Wise Choice of Toys* (University of Chicago Press, 1934).
[8] Chapter 15.
[9] Stuttering or a keyed-up, tense voice that bespeaks "tight" muscles in the upper throat.

is less difference between the rate of maturation and the demands of society in regard to speech. (After all, a very few months of delay at the age of one can throw a whole family into turmoil.)

Going back to the reflexes of prehension, running, hop scotch, et cetera, we see three sorts of reaction to retarded development. As he senses his inability to compete with his peers, the child often refuses to play ordinary games with others of his age or to go to school. Or as he seeks to "get back to a safe place," his fear may be expressed in regressive behavior. A third type of behavior (less frequently seen) is the development of leadership along some other line—the child often quite bullheadedly demanding that the play life be on his own terms. The destructive behavior of children for whom these reflexes develop too rapidly has been mentioned.[10]

As early as four or five children begin to feel uncomfortable about unusual stature. Therefore, we are interested in the incidence of atypical physical development and the social importance placed upon it.[11] This problem becomes more acute at school, where there is ample chance for comparison. Both boys and girls of precocious size are aware of being "out of place" and respond with various symptoms of resentment—truancy, rebellion, blasé indifference, and so forth. But in play life boys are often looked up to and given a place of leadership just because of superior physical development. We often forget, however, that this is a two-edged sword in that society often makes demands for integration and ability that such children can't meet. We unconsciously think of them as older than they really are.[12] Trends in the development of interest in competitive sports for girls may soon weigh the factors in the same relationship as for boys.

[10] See p. 31. The whole matter is discussed in Chapter 6.
[11] See White House Conference (Section I, Committee A).
[12] The average six-year-old who has the physique or facies of an eight-year-old often shows the same keyed-up, tense irritability that one sees in children who constantly associate with somewhat older playmates, even though his own playmates are of the six-year level.

Children (particularly boys, but won't this change as girls go more into competitive sports?) who are runts show every sort of compensatory reaction. The bitter, bullying reactions are as well known as the noisy overcompensating blusterings of this group.

The problem of atypical physical development becomes acute in an apparently different way in adolescence. The factors are precisely the same as those just mentioned, but the great social importance of sex seems to make them different. Now it is rather the girl who gains leadership through precocity—and of whom, so often, much more maturity is expected (or tacitly assumed) than she has attained.

Finally, there is the child's need to adjust to the authority of certain problems of glandular imbalance (e.g., in the pituitary or thyroid). Relatively little is known of this field, but there are unquestionably constellations of symptoms which run together and which have accumulated serious cultural loads[13]—such as femininity in boys. Two distinct sets of symptoms appear here: those that might reasonably be thought of as arising from the physical condition itself (as clumsiness or the lack of agility in hypopituitarism), and those that arise from the significance given to the various constellations by the culture, so that children "look" teaseable, effeminate, retarded in development. The reactions of the child are fractionated between his struggle in the midst of the physical difficulty itself, the limitations in response which this condition entails, and what society "thinks" he is. Thus in hypopituitarism (Fröhlich's syndrome) there are compensatory glandular adjustments at least in the thyroid; marked retardation in sexual maturation; clumsiness in fine coordinations; and overcompensations, various attention-getting devices, or delinquency as natural reactions to being thought a "sissy."[14]

---

[13] J. P. C. Griffith and A. G. Mitchell, *Textbook of Pediatrics* (Philadelphia, Saunders, 1941), pp. 899–931. Also Leo Kanner, *Child Psychiatry* (Springfield, Thomas, 1935), pp. 191–195. The latter reference deals mostly with rather exaggerated symptoms.

[14] This matter is discussed from a different angle in Chapter 14, pp. 174 f.

As the child moves into adolescence the symptoms previously sketched are the more marked because physically the child is "out of phase"—the homeostasis[15] that existed up to eight or nine will now be unbalanced for several years. The various physiological functions probably move at varying pace and without the fixed relationship to each other that earlier accompanied the "in phase" years. Thus a restless ill-at-easeness may be sandwiched between bursts of power and energy. Lackadaisical school work may appear side by side with flashes of enthusiasm as to fads or work. Or outstanding athletic achievement may be coupled with lazy, careless attitudes as to other physical demands.

At this time there also are the physiological changes dependent upon sexual maturation.[16] However, these are inextricably interwoven with the cultural pattern and can only be seen in this relationship. Physical development is less important as such than it is in relation to sophistication in attire. Therefore, all trends in cultural stratification of adolescent behavior are important.[17] To this the child reacts under one or more of four general headings. (1) He may brush aside all other problems by excelling in one area—such as athletics. (2) He may show his uncertainty in a kind of elephantine mischief—a clumsy intrusion into every sort of affair. (3) He may try to fight the matter out by resorting to daydreams. Here, obviously, he is free to make his world one in which he controls the threats of the authority of physical development. (4) He may construct a veneer over the whole problem, as when he attains social acceptance through delinquency. One frequently sees adolescents with unusual or even repulsive physical traits who have won entirely adequate social position as daring or adventuresome antagonists of the law. The reader may be right in asserting that this fourth reaction is the same as the first. They seem to me (and to the child) to be different.

[15] W. B. Cannon, "Organization for Physiological Homeostasis," *Physiological Reviews*, vol. 9, no. 3, pp. 399–431, July 1929.
[16] Young, pp. 403 ff.   [17] Young, pp. 408 ff.

During adolescence a new problem appears in that the sexual drive itself becomes so insistent; or rather, the sexual drive loses its diffused character and now centers much more definitely about the genital functions. The clinician is accustomed to see the child react to this in one or more of four different ways: (1) Narcissistic preoccupation with the growth and development of the secondary sex characters. (2) An urgent desire to "try out" these new forces and drives. Boys show this rather frankly (masturbation, tentative efforts at heterosexual activity, exhibitionism, sodomy, and so forth). In girls it may be that the sexual drive is considerably more diffused, which would account for the lack of evidence in regard to the overt acts that are so common among boys. (3) Every sort of substitute behavior in which a dynamic association has been set up between sexual expression and some other type of behavior such as delinquency.[18] (4) Owing to the questions which the child always has as to his adequacy,[19] and to the fact that these tend now to crystallize about his tentative sexual expressions, he thinks of any sort of difficulty in this one field as a total personal inadequacy. We often see at this time a pervasive and spreading feeling of incompetence. The child may retreat before this, may build compensations to hide it, or may escape the whole issue through one or another psychoneurosis.

Without summing up all these trends and reactions, it seems obvious that by the middle of the second decade fairly-well-crystallized mental attitudes have been established in regard to physical authority. These are of every shade between the two extremes of a constant defiance of the "rules of health" on the basis of "having a good time while one lives" and a ritualistic obedience to every known or suspected rule of healthy living.

It is difficult to say when the child first becomes aware of the

[18] These are what Healy terms "conflict cases." See William Healy and others, *Reconstructing Behavior in Youth* (New York, Knopf, 1929).
[19] Chapter 14.

authority of possession. The first envelopment of the mother's arms plainly says, "You are mine"—obviously more in terms of belongingness than of authority. Therefore, if we say that two is the age at which the authority of possession appears for the child, we mean only that, in our experience, it is then that the child seems to begin to tease out this complex from the rest of life. Whether children are really owned by their parents (rather than by the State) is not important. Actually the child has been treated since birth as a possession, and soon the statements that "I am your mother" or "You are my child" are used to get all manner of things done. Without question, however, trends in concepts of posessiveness and ownership, laws and traditions of the control which adults have over children and the extent to which a pattern looks upon children as economic assets, are important;[20] also rural as opposed to urban patterns, as children are so much more necessary in the economy of the farm.[21]

The usual reaction to too great pressure in this area takes the form of definite rebellion or of phantasy (anxious, panicky reactions are not seen). But most children, and particularly boys, tend to grow out from under possession at a pretty tender age. Thus by five the child is beginning to do things to shock his parents, to notify them that he is "tough" or that he does very terrible things. Because of its earlier strength, however, his elders continue to try to prolong the authority of possession just as they will later try to prolong the authority of age.

Another validator of personal authority is belongingness or "love." Here, once more a problem begins in the very first weeks of life, when the tremendous power of the security-giving device invites its use to get anything and everything done. Coercion through "Don't you love me?" has filled lives and books for

[20] *Trends,* pp. 777–779, 1444.

[21] *Trends,* pp. 515, 545, 755. I should guess that there are similar differences between pioneer and more settled patterns.

countless ages, and has been answered in every conceivable way as people have tried to unravel the belongingness side of security from the binding side.

The steps that are involved here are intimately bound into those of the problem of security and have been described in Chapter 1. In general we have found that children (not to speak of countless adults) confuse the belongingness and authority issues of "love," but this shows only as rebellion until they reach adolescence. That is, in his earlier years the child will simply turn against an overwhelming use of the authority aspect of security regardless of the effect on the belongingness aspect. During the middle teens, however, most children reveal definite confusion as to the issues involved—towering rebellion turning in a moment to tearful, dependent cuddling and back again—much to the disconcerted amazement of their parents.

Sometime during their very early years children begin to feel the authority of age. At first they seem to lean upon this and to build it into their pattern ("My mother knows better because she is older"). Later, if there is too much pressure, we see children rebel, develop bully reactions towards younger children, or retire into phantasy life. Because age bulks so large in the authority problems of children we are interested in trends in our cultural pattern which stress its importance,[22] and especially in those which stress age in relation to school grades, obtaining work, and so forth.[23]

At three or four the child recognizes that he meets this same authority of age in other children—who generally use it in full recognition of its power. The data from the field of recreation in regard to the part that age plays in children's games[24] are im-

[22] *Trends*, pp. 26–37.
[23] R. G. Fuller, "Child Labor," *Annals of the American Academy of Political and Social Science*, vol. 212, p. 150, November 1940.
[24] *Trends*, p. 789.

portant, as are those in regard to the member rôles of the eldest children—both in the usual family and in families broken by death or desertion.

By five or six the child meets the same problem at school, where (frequently even on the college level) there is a temptation to teachers to "borrow" the authority so effectively used by the parents. So we are interested in changing conceptions in the school as to teacher-child relationships[25] and in trends towards looking upon the school as a social federation rather than as a family.[26] If there is too much pressure here, the child reacts in many different ways, though these tend to cluster about definite rebellion rather than about the anxious, panicky states that characterize insecurity.

During adolescence the child begins to direct his rebellion against his elders as well as against their demands. It is true that he still slavishly follows age in his worship of older children— but this seems to be a response to sophistication rather than to age. He has reached the point where he feels that adults no longer understand him or his needs, and where he questions any belief or tenet of the older generation. The trends of greatest importance here are those which regulate the period of adolescence and so advance or delay the time when the individual can take an active, productive part in the society in which he lives.[27] If, with the sociologist, we define adolescence as "that period that intervenes between physical maturation and society's acknowledgment of that maturity," then civilization might be defined as a process that constantly lengthens adolescence. In this sense we must recognize the dramatic shortening of adolescence during the war years and the inevitable lengthening which these next years will see.

Certainly a good deal of what we have described in this coun-

[25] *Trends,* pp. 782 f.; Prescott, pp. 267–272.   [26] Prescott, pp. 272–280.
[27] *Trends,* p. 303. See also Fuller, *loc. cit.*

try as the conflict between New and Old World cultures is, in reality, a somewhat comfortable way of closing one's eyes to the more disturbing interpersonal tensions that are involved. But this is not the end of the story. Each of the struggles with the authority of age—each of the outcomes—plays its part in the expression of that authority which the child will employ later as he becomes the parent.

Somewhere around three or four the child begins to realize, and to have to adjust himself to, the power of things beyond human control or understanding. This might be called "extra-human" authority.[28] His first contacts with this problem are indirect —his awe or fear of death being unquestionably acquired through association with adults. It is difficult to say just how soon he becomes acutely aware of his helplessness in the face of time, death, natural disaster, or deformity, but he certainly does so before adolescence. There are at least three matters that, in our experience, have some effect upon the age at which this change occurs: (1) The child with a sufficient sense of belongingness in his own family seems to find less difficulty in adjusting to this extra-human authority. It is as though he said, "I'm sure my parents are taking care of that." It would be nice if this could be measured by the age of church membership or of going to services or Sunday school, but there are too many other factors (e.g., what is proper in one's neighborhood) to make this a fair measure. Certain trends in these matters have been pictured,[29] but I doubt that they are the ones that are most significant. (2) It is important that the outstanding religious formulations in our culture were developed in rural settings, where the imminence of extra-human authority is far more pressing than in urban areas. However,

[28] As good a discussion as I have seen of the matters of this paragraph is given by C. A. Wise, *Religion in Illness and Health* (New York, Harper, 1942), pp. 135–170.
[29] *Trends*, pp. 1033–1039.

these same formulations are being bent to new ends stressing social responsibility and social reform, and one increasingly wonders how far the child can look to them now for an answer to the problems created by extra-human authority.[30] (3) Finally the matter has to be measured against the growing availability of many "causes" that can carry heavy belongingness loads. Various youth movements meet this issue—perhaps the most notable being that which the Nazi group fostered in Germany.

Extra-human authority thus becomes the child's "own" problem at different ages for different individuals, yet there is certainly one constant factor. The problem is sharper and more pressing for the rural than for the city child. So we are interested in those population shifts that are from rural to urban areas (or vice versa).[31] What the child does by way of adjusting to this problem it would be impossible even to outline. In recording here eight types of reaction we are simply showing children, as we often see them, in the process of building a philosophy of life. (1) Some accept extra-human authority as they accept clothes or air. If you ask them about it, they say it "just is" and seem to go no further. (2) Some project themselves into extra-human authority. "Accidents occur in threes," "It will be just my luck to. . . ." (3) Some forever complain about it: "Why am I a girl?" "Why must I die?" This whining attitude seeps into all corners of their lives. (4) Some adopt bully reactions—taking it out on others whenever they can. In our experience, this is the only one of the eight reactions that involves delinquency. Individuals go to every conceivable length to pay back for "what God has done" to them. (5) If a child has never had any serious reverses and then suffers two or three major catastrophes that seem to him utterly incomprehensible, one sometimes gets the picture of his being stunned, dazed, confused. (6) Some seem rather "willfully" to go into what

30 For these changing objectives in the Church today, see *Trends,* pp. 1010–1016.
31 *Trends,* p. 12.

we are pleased to call a psychosis as their only solution. We have seen Ganser's syndrome[32] developing and other more permanent states that appear to belong in the dementia praecox group. (7) Some construct for themselves (and usually do not hesitate to impose it on others) a sort of working hypothesis. (8) Some turn to the various answers that religious formulations have given (e.g., a personal God who is watching and caring). In the presence of very serious events—such as death—most children turn to this reaction. It would be quite exciting to know the reason. We have supposed that it follows a pattern given to them very early by their parents and, on this basis, presents itself as the simplest and most enveloping mode of response.

Just as the child must adjust to personal and extra-human authority, he must eventually submit to the authority of the group. This last phase validates itself, so far as the child is concerned, through numbers ("what everybody is doing"). He clearly recognizes this by seven or eight, but obviously its roots run back into earlier years (e.g., I have seen children almost hypnotically compelled to join in group activity at kindergarten, but I haven't been able, at that level, to get a child to verbalize this as "social authority"). It is our experience that there are five general types of reaction to the authority of numbers. (1) We see a slavish sort of following which is not difficult for the child unless the social division is so even that he cannot clearly discern a majority opinion. This last leads to the same sort of panicky "I-don't-know-what-to-do" that animals show when two conditioned reflexes interfere with each other. (2) There may be an equally slavish effort at always "being different." I have assumed that these chronic rebels (many persistent and noisy "radicals" are of this type) had unfortunate group experiences early in life, but I lack adequate proof from enough cases. (3) We see an anxious and tense confu-

[32] Bernard Glueck, *Studies in Forensic Psychiatry* (Boston, Little, 1916), pp. 66 ff.

sion when the authority of numbers conflicts with other authorities. This is illustrated by the youngster who goes to college well adjusted to extra-human authority (say in terms of a personal God) and finds that the predominant adjustment of the new group is in one of the other categories mentioned above.[33] (4) A similar anxious and tense confusion may appear when the authority of numbers conflicts with the child's previous patterns or fairly-well-established personal goals as, for instance, when a high school youngster who has been very "properly" brought up meets majority acceptance of petting or other liberties and interests. (5) Just as in the realm of extra-human authority adjustments, the child may try to escape in one or more of many ways—his withdrawal showing as shyness, reserve, "lone wolf" retreat, or frankly psychotic behavior that in general follows the pattern of schizophrenia.

Because personal authority (possession, belongingness, and age) becomes less important relatively early in the child's life, the authority of numbers carries a large fraction of the cultural imprint. This starts long before he is aware of it, for even in infancy, when personal authority is the sole issue, he will be told by his mother that *most* children don't wet the bed, *most* children say "please." As the child grows there appear countless formal and informal agencies to impress upon him the authority of numbers (e.g., the radio assured millions each day that most people were more tolerant than Hitler).[34] However, it is during adolescence that the child dramatically and acutely faces the issue. At this time social authority extends to every item of appearance, behavior, and goal,[35] and a great many adolescents welcome pre-

---

[33] See p. 40.

[34] This is beautifully illustrated in its relation to consumers' problems in *Trends,* Chapter XVII, particularly pp. 871–884.

[35] For this point in the physical field there is an excellent bibliography in Young, p. 403. For the field of behavior (Courtship, etc.) see Young, p. 473. For these two fields and that of the setting up of every sort of "ism" as a control for goals and values see the excellent case records in Peter Blos, *The Adolescent Personality* (New York, Appleton-Century, 1941).

cisely this situation—their vulnerability and at-sea-ness often finding that what most people are doing is a welcome, not-to-be-questioned guide.

Out of all his reactions to the authority of numbers the adult builds a fairly stabilized pattern of adjustment, but this is no place to explore it—beyond pointing out two trends which are important in that they further open the way for impressing social authority on young children. The first is represented in the growth of nursery schools;[36] the second, in the imposition of methods of bringing up children (ways of feeding them, ways of controlling their behavior) through pointing out what most people are or should be doing.[37] But this doesn't comprehend the full sweep of social authority, which is very definitely carried to the child by his parents through personal authority (that of possession, belongingness, and age). From the start the adult sees in these personal validators a means by which he can translate the authority of numbers to the child. But it is precisely this change that is resisted by the child, who clings to the reality and permanence of the earlier personal authority, never really wanting to accept the fact that in the pattern in which he lives social authority is the power to which he must adjust.

The whole question of social sanction must be considered in relation to Chapter 4. As each person must slavishly follow the authority of numbers, he must also feel that he is different from everyone else.

Social authority also validates itself through those who are acclaimed. So at about the same time that he adjusts to the authority of numbers, each child meets special problems in the acceptance or rejection of the styles, behavior, or values of various heroes. Obviously this is one aspect of the authority of numbers, as

---

[36] *Trends,* p. 788.

[37] H. L. Witmer, *Psychiatric Clinics for Children* (New York, Commonwealth Fund, 1940), Chapter 3, particularly p. 56.

acclaim involves the approval of large or important groups. A separate section is devoted to it because: (1) The authority of numbers is so definitely personalized here—and thus given acute, specific driving power. (2) The person acclaimed often has characteristics which are not acclaimed but which the child follows in the identifying process. (3) While the authority of numbers continues to control in pretty tyrannical fashion throughout life, the authority of acclaim runs the hazard of what we are pleased to call disillusionment, in which it is apparent that "people are not what they are cracked up to be."[38]

So we are interested in the extent to which the newspaper, radio, movies, and so forth have increased the number of "heroes," have affected the length of time that they are in the public eye, and have determined the type of person or characteristic that is given prominence, and the same goes for the schoolroom use of the lives of heroes as paradigms for children.

The child's method of copying is much the same as for the authority of numbers in general. There is often a slavish following of details of dress and behavior—at times in grotesquely exaggerated fashion. There may be an equally slavish effort at not being like the acclaimed person in any way. There are often phantasied identifications with traits of the acclaimed person, with no overt action or with only fragmentary bits of overt action. Sometimes there is a rather cold or intellectual selection of traits which seem valuable to the child—and copying of these.

Another validator of social authority is accomplishment. Persons who achieve much are often those who are acclaimed, so that everything in the previous section applies here too. There is, however, a very important difference—that in "acclaim" society decides who is great, whereas in "accomplishment" it is the child himself who decides what persons have benefited society. In other

[38] Plant, pp. 214 ff.

words, here the child is free to project his own drives and goals into what he believes to be the social authority that presses upon him. So an adolescent may slavishly copy some rather eccentric soul because he sees in this person's philosophy a point he feels to be of great social value. It is probably safe to say that where the child recognizes the success or contributions of individuals who have been generally acclaimed we can follow the statements of the previous section; but where he sees such accomplishment (which leads to identification) in a person not acclaimed by the group, we can assume that the youngster has not made a good adjustment to, or has been rebellious against, all social authority.

CHAPTER 3

Status Preservation

We see children who have the problem of building an ego that is a sort of castle and of protecting this ego from intruders of all kinds by means of a sort of "wall," the height and thickness of which are apparently dependent upon the character of the assaults that the ego experiences or looks forward to. We do not know how much of this reserve—of keeping one's ego inviolable —is normal. This "wall that preserves one's status"[1] probably changes constantly during each day and is at its point of maximum efficiency and assistance when it allows the individual freedom to work out his own internal problems without interference and yet does not shut out assistance and valuable challenges which the environment constantly offers him.

This wall is not the same as the envelope which is mentioned frequently throughout this volume. Both operate at the periphery of the personality, and when inviolability is seriously threatened both mechanisms seem to provide complete protection from outside influences in somewhat the same way. But the envelope is a translating mechanism operating in a bio-osmotic manner, whereas the status-preserving mechanism is a fending-off affair, operating to rebuff or parry in a quite mechanical way. When the child is sorely pressed by the busyness of his environment, only a sophist would try to decide which mechanism is at work in the matter of protection; the two seem to move into each other, to

[1] It is unfortunate that I have felt forced to use the term status in a certain specific way in this chapter when it already had a definite, and somewhat different, meaning in sociological literature. It is further unfortunate that the two definitions overlap.

overlap completely. However, under free and easy conditions, the wall of status preservation entirely disappears, whereas the envelope continues actively to interpret each phenomenon.

The origin and early history of this status-preserving mechanism has been so fully described elsewhere[2] that very few words should be required here. It is apparently developed during the first year or two as the individual "defines" himself from his environment. Psychoanalytical theory describes the mechanism of cathexis as an intensification of the emotional load upon the individual when the environment withdraws from what the infant first conceived to be his ego. My own view is quite the opposite— that this intensification is more actively brought about by the individual through the gradual delimitation of his own personality. With such a history one can understand why from the age of two there should be fear and rebuff of meddlesome approach, for which the phenomenon of cathexis in no way accounts.

Negativism in young children is the opposite of cuddliness. One feels the muscular withdrawal of the child. The most interesting place to watch it is in a kindergarten or first grade where, as children gather about anything of interest, they pack in together like so many sardines. The negativistic child, the one who has been "kept at" too much, does not sit off in the corner as the shy one does, but he always maintains a little distance between himself and the group. The tendency of the wall of status to thicken at the physical approach of others is perhaps the chief way in which it differs from the shyness of reserve or introversion.[3] With complete strangers, however, the phenomenon may immediately lessen or even entirely disappear. Obviously all through life a person is caught between this basic fear of an intrusion upon his personality and the widespread propaganda that

[2] Plant, pp. 120–127. Also J. S. Plant, "Negativism: Its Treatment and Its Implications," *American Journal of Diseases of Children*, vol. 61, no. 2, pp. 358–368, February 1941.
[3] Chapter 11.

the better we know people the better we like them. So educators insistently call for the "breaking down of barriers," and the people ever more rapidly build barriers—of intolerance, suspicion, and hatred. When the barriers are broken down slowly and with gentleness—well, that's different, as every parent knows.

The second stage of the status-preserving mechanism—the development of defensive lying—may begin appearing when the child is three or four. This may or may not be a substitution of the verbal, for the earlier muscular form of expression, as many adults still "protect themselves" in the tightening, withdrawing, psychomotor fashion that is characteristic of the first phase of development. Once more, however, the problem is "mechanical" in that the lies are in direct proportion to the threat. The child is often at perfect ease in disclosing to a stranger something which he defends by constant lying to those who sit at each meal with him or who "keep after" him about each detail of his life. Much of whatever success the psychiatrist may have I am sure is due to the fact that the patient knows that in this purely mechanical fashion what he tells "cannot be used against him." This need of the child to feel that his relationship with the psychiatrist or social worker is inviolate is one of the main reasons for developing teams in psychiatric therapy. When one person works with the child and another with the parent, there is tacit assurance to the young patient that his confidences will not be retailed.[4]

The third stage is a sort of combination and refinement of the first two—that impervious, blasé, heedless manner which drives us parents and teachers to distraction. Little of it appears before adolescence. For lack of a better term, I call it the "water-off-the-

[4] The pediatrician is at a serious disadvantage in the field of conduct disorders not only because he is employed by the parents but also because the child has been accustomed to going to him with a parent. In general, he has failed so far to establish himself as the child's doctor—rather than he whom the family employs to keep the child well (and properly behaving!). Pediatricians, very rightly, wish to enter more into the field of conduct disorders, but they cannot get very far until they have met the issue covered in this note.

duck's-back" mechanism. The child sees us and hears what we say, but our words don't seem ever to be taken in—they flow over him without any other effect than of assuring him of the efficacy of his protection.

As the individual grows up he habituates his use of one, or two, or all of these three methods. I don't know what are the bases of choice. Judging, however, from my older clinic children and from chance observation of my peers, it seems safe to say that somewhere in adolescence each one does choose a method of pre-serving inviolability and that he pretty much sticks to it through the years.

There is a constant search for situations in which the problem of status preservation can be dropped, if only momentarily; and the whole mechanism is often depersonalized by means of various symbols and conventions.[5] It is as though man had found the load too heavy and had built other means of carrying it. I understand that impersonal modes of announcing and preserving status are developed to a very high degree among primitive tribes. This would seem natural in view of the intimacy of primitive life and the absence there of means of getting away from others.

There will appear below certain situations in which the wall of status preservation completely melts away. I have taken the speed and ease with which the wall disappears and is rebuilt as further indications (wouldn't it be nice if for once one could prove something in this field?) that the whole business is a rather mechanical affair—not running deep into the basic structure of the personality. But it is none the less important because it thus appears to be one of the ways in which the personality acts rather than one of the things of which the personality is composed.

I see little clinical evidence of this wall before the second year

[5] This chapter perhaps gives an inadequate appraisal of the subject, which is discussed more fully in Plant, pp. 156, 157.

and think of it as not being well established before the fourth, but I am sure that it is in process of formation by the eighth or ninth month[6]—the way having been prepared by the withdrawal of the environment in large and small sectors.[7] The fact that this occurs so early in life makes the child's defenses especially vulnerable to environmental pressures. Consequently there are important trends in the number of adults surrounding the child in the home,[8] in the education of adults as to the extent to which their interference with this process (their "bossiness") affects the mechanism[9] and in the development of play groups for very young children.[10]

The reaction of the child to too much pressure, to the adults' failure to allow him to form his own protected ego, has been described above[11] and need be only mentioned here. Up to the age of four the dominant note is that of "negativism"—of not "melting into" or cuddling against other people. Then a new form begins to appear—the child's answer of "no" to everything that is proposed. By six persistent protective lying develops. By ten there may begin to appear the "water-off-the-duck's-back" mechanism —a blasé, I-didn't-hear-you attitude.

As the child gets to the point where he begins to be aware of his own conflicts, and where he wants to shut out any interfer-

[6] By then the child's facial expression seems to indicate that he is beginning to separate himself from the environment—in the dimmest way to be starting to be a separate entity. If you work a great deal with very young children you feel that it is about this time that the baby ceases to be a mirror and begins to become a person.

[7] That is, while it must be evident that I believe that the wall of status preservation is not formed by cathexis (as the psychoanalysts believe), the latter phenomenon is of prime importance in laying the groundwork for a mechanism that protects the ego from too harsh an intrusion.

[8] *Trends*, pp. 681–684. This diminution in the size of the household must always be seen as a different matter from that of the size of the family (of the number of children).

[9] For instance in such books as B. I. Beverly, *In Defense of Children* (New York, Day, 1941).

[10] *Trends*, p. 788   [11] See pp. 47 f.

ence with his preoccupations, the mechanism is more definitely and consciously controlled from within. The trends (and the responses on the child's part) are essentially those given in the previous section except as the fact of the individual's growing control gives certain new coloring.

The simplest of these new forms is the response "Oh, don't bother me—I have troubles of my own." A great deal of what we ordinarily call shyness is really this wall built to preserve status (in the child's own eyes) even in the midst of quite overwhelming odds.[12] By now there is, of course, more emphasis on such dynamisms as reserve, fending off, calculated falsifications, braggadocio, and so forth.[13]

Throughout childhood there are many situations which invite a temporary thinning of the wall. Two types are discernible: (1) There are certain crises or situations in which the child "opens his heart." All along the way into adolescence these sudden bursts of confidence appear—though less and less frequently, more impulsively and with ever less predictability. Very often, though by no means always, the child weeps at such times, and one can feel a certain relaxation or softening of the muscle tone. The exciting event is usually rich in emotional content—keen disappointment or hurt or unbounded joy over something. On more occasions than I should like to admit, I have been given full and accurate accounts of the whole situation by children who, I discovered

[12] The differential diagnosis often has to build on therapeutic developments— removal of adult pressures. Where one can still the torrent of parental directions and questions and can get the teacher to say always "Let's sing" (to the group) instead of "You sing" (to the child), these walls of status preservation melt with great rapidity. This does not occur with the forms of shyness that belong to introversion (Chapter 11) or to inadequacy (Chapter 14).

[13] It is at least possible that the schizophrenic, so busily working out his own problems, is really separated from reality by the fear that he may be looked in upon. This possibility is most dramatically inviting in the catatonic form, where there is such a large component of the physical stiffening that is apparent in the very early childhood years of this problem.

later, had been warned they were going to "the man who can see right through you," and that therefore they had "better tell the truth." (2) There are certain persons who, for reasons we don't understand, seem to elicit the deepest confidence of the child. We all know such people, but, so far as I am aware, no study has been made of their characteristics or methods. The trends that are significant are those in the recognition of the importance of this positive transference in such groups as teachers and social workers.[14]

At about the age of six the child starts pushing back the wall to include his family or some other group that is close to him. Apparently all through life—the "inclosed areas" become larger and the bonds more varied (e.g., gang, fraternity, college, some form of business, social class, race, or nationality). Because the child is older as this phase of the problem develops, we see fewer of the physical symptoms of withdrawal or negativism here, and more lying, braggadocio, blasé reactions, and the like. If we use three illustrative examples (with the critical trends for these) a great many others will immediately come to mind. At the level of the family this mechanism is affected by the solidarity of the clan or family group.[15] Further on, the integration of the child's gang life is important—and the significant trends are those in the development of close-knit as opposed to loosely tied gang formation, affected by the juxtaposition of different racial groups.[16] An example of more recently developed homogeneous groups would

[14] Prescott, pp. 267 ff.; also all through the case material in F. H. Allen, *Psychotherapy with Children* (New York, Norton, 1942).

[15] Trends in this are those of the disappearance of the clan family (see footnote 26, p. 17) and the effect upon this of the dispersion of the functions of the family (*Trends*, pp. 666–679).

[16] F. M. Thrasher, *The Gang* (University of Chicago Press, 1927), Chapter IV. Gangs amongst racial groups that are threatened by the presence of other racial groups tend to be more close-knit.

be those of distinct social status (e.g., a few "blue blood" families in a rapidly industrializing area).

Somewhere around the beginning of the school experience the child starts going through this same problem (showing precisely the same reactions to it) with other groups besides the family (e.g., the neighborhood). Trends in population concentration are important here.[17] Our own experience is that the "wall" is thickest in suburban neighborhoods and in apartment-house communities—being considerably less so in very crowded city areas (where the very congestion seems to lend anonymity) and also much less so in rural areas. In a general way, when the individual is in a situation where he meets a person whom he has never seen and will never see again, this wall may become much thinner or lower—often to a remarkable degree. We can afford to let people in, if they are not going to stay. This is the reason, as stated above, that many problems can be worked out with a comparative stranger (e.g., a psychiatrist) that cannot be solved in usual surroundings.

One sees this rather dramatically in the tendency that appears by the age of ten or twelve to form a "spiritual" rather than a geographical neighborhood—to build a set of companions who are far enough away so that their association is not a constant mechanical threat. The important trends are those in the roaming range of children,[18] those in the formation of clubs which are not built on a neighborhood basis (e.g., high school fraternities), or those in facilities for transportation.[19]

Meanwhile, at the age of eight or ten, the use of certain symbols has begun to take over some of the functions of the wall of status

[17] *Trends,* pp. 12–17. [18] *Trends,* pp. 167–181, 456.
[19] *Trends,* Chapter IV up to p. 203.

preservation. In our cultural pattern school marks or school grade, clothes, or social position often indicate that "no questions need be asked." In other cultures, where even more extrapersonal facts care for status, the personal mechanism should disappear even more quickly.

The importance and prestige of this depersonalization of the problem of status preservation, grows rapidly with age. Note here the trends in advertising towards proclaiming that goods "will tell who you are."[20] We are also interested in the economic swings, since it is easy and inviting to use these impersonal aids in "good times" and difficult to do so in times of depression.[21] Uniforms and insignia are of enormous help here—it's amazing what questions one gold bar will keep from being asked.[22]

As adolescence sharpens the problem of sexualization there are no qualitative differences in the picture, but there is a very definite intensification of the mechanism. This, in our experience, is more marked in girls than in boys, being particularly true of the six-to-twelve-month period just preceding the establishment of menstruation. As one would expect, for each new problem or new intricacy of life to be met, a more dependable and foolproof machinery for fending off any possible intruders must be created. The trends in coeducation and other formal modes of throwing the two sexes together are important here. So are those in the development of many means of competition and social relationship (such as athletics) that do not have primary sexual meanings.[23]

Two matters in particular should be stressed. (1) Adolescence is normally marked by an increased sensitivity—a feeling of increasing vulnerability to the pressures of the environment. One

[20] This runs all through *Trends*, pp. 871–896.   [21] *Trends*, pp. xxix ff., 265 ff.
[22] There are interesting trends here in the formation of overt or secret organizations involving elaborate insignia and titles (*Trends*, pp. 935 ff.).
[23] *Trends*, pp. 925–933.

sees this in the growing importance of clothes, family finances, and so forth—with an acute need to hide any differences that set the individual apart. (2) Then, too, sexual interests take on the force of a primary drive in addition to their earlier symbolic significance,[24] thus involving the mechanism of status preservation in an intricate series of approach and withdrawal reactions. In this connection it would be interesting to have data in regard to trends affecting the age of sexualization[25] and those hastening the cadence of life, so that the symbols of being grown up are used without regard to physical maturing. In general it seems as though the children of today are doing about the same things that we did, but about two years earlier. On the other hand social responsibility in the form of gainful employment seems to be delayed.[26]

The problem of adjusting the wall of status preservation to the phenomena of intimacy and sexual expression begins with adolescence and continues through life. There are two aspects to this —running into each other but capable of separation for our present purposes.

The first has to do with the necessity of preserving this wall despite the "myth of romanticism," which teaches that there should be no reservations in the love relationship. Consequently, if the close approach of another person thickens or raises this wall, what happens in the development of the love ties? Here trends in acceptance of the myth, with its picture of complete and free interchange between two people, are paralleled by trends in the social and economic independence of women.[27]

The second aspect involves the sexual act itself. In the relationship of intimacy the wall of status preservation for once com-

24 Chapters 9 and 10.
25 Is this occurring earlier, as Stanley Hall claimed?
26 *Trends*, p. 303. Note the sharp reversal in this during the war years.
27 *Trends*, pp. 711–716.

pletely disappears—only to be rebuilt when satisfaction is attained. These rapid shifts in adjustment represent a serious task for the personality. Because of the youth of our patients, my clinical data on this subject are limited, but it seems obvious that the problem would be sharpened as the sexual act served less as a means of physical satisfaction or of procreation and more as an expression of personal relationship.[28] Trends in the latter direction are therefore important, and so are trends in birth control and the knowledge of contraceptives, as these allow the sexual act to become more and more an expression of the relation of one personality to another.[29]

Also during adolescence—perhaps a little before—the youngster undergoes certain experiences that markedly, if only temporarily, modify this wall. These are new experiences, and he unquestionably turns to them with conscious relief because they offer a chance to relax his eternal vigilance. Four illustrations will do. There are those informal gatherings of small groups in which the individuals feel in perfect communication "though not a word is said."[30] One gets the same feeling in crowds with a single purpose, protest groups, at games, and in various kinds of teamwork.[31] Marching and other stereotyped experiences in large groups do the same thing.[32] Also, there is the effect produced by music and dancing. Note, for instance, the "singleness" of an audience at a symphony concert—which singleness is broken up immediately the music stops and talking begins.

Finally, we can well raise an important speculative question

[28] Chapters 9 and 10.   [29] *Trends*, p. 43.

[30] The reader will understand that my own theories would mean that this should read "because not a word is said," rather than "though not a word is said," that words are one of the surest and most inviting structural units for this wall.

[31] This is nicely illuminated in E. D. Martin, *The Behavior of Crowds* (New York, Harper, 1920).

[32] Trends in regimentation as in various totalitarian set-ups are important here. *Trends*, pp. 1534 ff.

about which there are no data at present—namely, whether changes in member rôles[33] (e.g., the father as a bread-winner) place heavier personal loads in the matter of preserving and strengthening the wall. This should be the case; for though member rôles are established and maintained by informal means, they yet remain very important means of defining status, of fending off questions. We thought we saw something of this during the last depression,[34] when the father's loss of his traditional position as bread-winner meant a growing aloofness from others, since he now had to appear to them as more of a person. The protection of relatively well-established member rôles must be similar to that of insignia or uniforms—but of course on a much more subtle basis.

[33] See footnote 16, p. 13.   [34] Also see *Trends,* pp. 696–705.

CHAPTER 4

The Feeling of Difference

We see children who have a compelling drive at whatever cost to feel different from everybody else. Sometimes this takes the form of feeling worse than others (e.g., of being the "worst child in the neighborhood"). The feeling that one is an individual, and as such idiomatic, is served well by the sense of guilt. This is why the latter is so hard to dissipate. A child will struggle to have others see him as he sees himself and to agree that his problems are uniquely complicated and stubborn. He asks reassurance, but cannot accept this because it fundamentally strikes at his sense of difference.

It will be obvious that this view of the matter is at complete variance with that of the psychoanalysts. The conception here is that the feeling of difference is primary[1] and that this is identified with and strengthened by the feelings of guilt to be dramatically expressed in terms of the latter.[2] Freud assumed the sense of guilt to be quite separate from that of individuality, postulating rather that the former arises from the Oedipus situation, which he blithely accepted as being fixed upon man by "fate."[3]

I have not seen anywhere in the literature a recognition of the symbiosis that exists between the sense of guilt and the sense of being an individual, of being different.[4] This is odd because it is

[1] Clyde Kluckhohn and W. H. Kelly give the anthropologists' agreement with this view. See "The Concept of Culture" in *The Science of Man in the World Crisis*, edited by Ralph Linton, pp. 78–106, particularly p. 103 (New York, Columbia University Press, 1945). This whole chapter should be required reading for students interested in the relationship between personality and culture.

[2] Plant, pp. 165–167. [3] Healy, p. 130.

[4] This is not quite a fair statement, as L. G. Lowrey ("Competitions and the Con-

common experience that patients would almost prefer to give up life than to give up the sense of guilt. True enough they come begging to be rid of its burden, but once it is gone the individual feels that he has no distinguishing mark, that he is lost in the group. All this is said in full recognition of the sorrow and tragedy that stem from each individual's fear of accepting himself as himself and in the hope that some day we shall be able to see ourselves as different without seeing ourselves as alone.

This matter of being set apart comes to the infant in subtle but insistent ways through the psychomotor tensions of the adults who appear in his life, so that much depends on methods used in early habit-training[5] (e.g., the question whether praise for good rather than punishment for bad would not largely do away with the use of the sense of guilt as an individualizing factor). The recent rise of the specialty of pediatrics has significantly affected the trends here. We now realize that until the early 1930's pediatricians were unwittingly increasing parental anxiety by their interest in "correct" weight and the fixed and carefully scheduled rhythms of feeding and excretion.

Before the age of four the child definitely crystallizes the notion that he is distinct from his environment.[6] This occurs at a time when parents are very likely to be stating the child's individuality in terms of his being worse, or more trouble, than other children. This anxious concern on the part of the parents arises from a realization of their own inadequacies and from a very natural desire to achieve perfection in the area of their chief preoccupation. Where the pressure bears too hard upon the

flict over Difference," *Mental Hygiene*, vol. 12, no. 2, pp. 316–330, April 1928) opens the door to the possibility.

[5] These are hard to measure statistically, but they can be seen in the more recent books of leading pediatricians, such as C. A. and M. M. Aldrich, *Babies Are Human Beings* (New York, Macmillan, 1938) or B. I. Beverly, *In Defense of Children* (New York, Day, 1941).

[6] Chapter 3.

child's deficiencies or abilities one sees "nervous," anxious, jittery reactions. The trends to consider here are those in family and nursery school attitudes towards individualizing the child through his accomplishments rather than his defects[7] and those in the development of nursery schools,[8] since the teacher does not "have so much at stake" so far as each child is concerned.[9]

At three or four the child begins to differentiate between himself as a "good child" and as a "bad child." As stated elsewhere,[10] such explanations as "The bad child did that, but he has gone now," probably only echo adult remarks, which thus serve as a convenient way of handling discipline without threatening the child too much in these earliest years. As he begins to identify himself more definitely with the "good parent" or the "bad parent" (perhaps at seven or eight), isolation of his "bad" self may be the only way in which he can bear to contemplate his faults. We see this carried all through life in such dualisms as "the soul and the body" or "the spirit and the flesh." The trends are difficult to treat statistically but are none the less real—in teaching (e.g., by church, school, or movies) as to good and evil as separate and struggling forces.

As the problem thus defines itself in terms of failure or wrongdoing, it is often expressed only in the youngster's phantasy life. This is difficult to uncover, though some children resort to adventuresome behavior in search of new experience. Others strive to prove themselves better than they think the world believes them to be. They are forever "turning over a new leaf." As older children they rush from one to another fad of attire or behavior

---

[7] See above, note 5.   [8] *Trends,* p. 788.

[9] A teacher has to repair the mistakes of her life quite as much as does any parent. However, the teacher does not have the insistent invitation that is offered by one's own child, in this respect. Moreover, at worst the teacher has intimate contact with any particular child for only about one year.

[10] Chapter 8, pp. 104 f.

in an effort at getting a "fresh start." Like the sense of guilt the sense of inadequacy is extremely strong and an important prop to the feeling of individuality.

The sense of guilt receives a commanding drive through its association with the problem of sibling rivalry,[11] at an early age. However universal this phenomenon is, every tradition and teaching we have interdicts it in severe terms. The child finds it frowned upon by adults from the beginning, but it is our own experience that he does not consciously and directly[12] reproach himself for rivalry feelings until he is six or seven. The reaction is one of atonement—whether expressed in terms of driving himself on towards perfection (as in the previous section), or of sweet and compliant attitudes towards the parents, or of oversolicitous tenderness towards the siblings.

However, I have been less interested in defining the form taken by the sense of guilt in these early years than in the fact that it seems to originate as the youngster is becoming preoccupied with the important matter of separating himself out and apart from the rest of his environment. The sharp decrease in the size of the family (and the growing incidence of one-child families), along with parental interest in spacing children,[13] should make a difference in the pictures of sibling rivalry. Obviously the problem is absent for the only child, and in theory it should be absent when children are very widely spaced. But in our experience wide spacing does not do away with acute sibling rivalry, though it delays its first appearance for any individual (often keeping it entirely out of the picture through the first four or five years). There was a very high birth rate during the war years,

11 Chapter 20.
12 With these two adverbs I should like to separate the child's recognition of sibling rivalry as a primary problem from his realization that it is something which disturbs him because it brings disfavor upon him from his parents or other adults.
13 *Trends,* pp. 683 ff.

but what the ultimate effect will be we don't know. Will an appreciable number of these young families go on as hurriedly to the second and third child, or will there be a return to a more leisurely and studied spacing? Another trend of great importance here is the recent widespread teaching that sibling rivalry is a natural (if, indeed, somewhat disconcerting) part of children's growth.[14]

Throughout the development of the sexual urge[15] the stage is being set for the further dramatization of the sense of guilt. It is hard to know just when this begins. If the child realizes in early babyhood that parents are displeased when he handles his genitalia, certainly by four or five he can consciously associate a much more sharply localized feeling of sexual satisfaction with the feeling of guilt that parents give to it. We will find in Chapter 9 that the steps are diffuse feelings of disturbance, diffuse feelings of pleasure, and centered feelings of pleasure. In children of about six, then, we begin to see either covert, shy, solitary ruminations or explosive bits of misconduct that will surely bring the punishment the child feels he should have because he is "such a bad person." The many trends that indicate a decrease in the social implications of sexual life[16] and an increase in its personal implications are of the greatest importance here, since they directly affect the extent to which adults press their ban on any form of sexual expression. To the psychiatrist it should be obvious that the startling changes in the rôle of the family and the rapid increase in contraceptive knowledge are constantly decreasing the sociological load which the sexual act earlier carried.

---

[14] This is hard to measure but might be considered in terms of the growing number of such books as Irma Weill, *About Tom* (New York, Island Workshop, 1941).

[15] Used here in the sense of Chapter 9.

[16] Young, p. 483. See also Ruth Benedict, "Some Comparative Data on Culture and Personality with Reference to the Promotion of Mental Health," in *Mental Health,* edited by F. R. Moulton and P. O. Komora (Lancaster, American Association for the Advancement of Science, 1939).

As the child reaches adolescence, the sense of guilt becomes fully wedded to the feeling of difference—of individuality. There are such heavy social pressures operating in the field of sex that he is convinced that no one else in the world could have such bad thoughts or could be "such a worm." As pointed out in the introduction to this chapter, this creates a great difficulty in the area of therapy, because anxious as the child is to be rid of the intolerable burden of guilt, it seems more and more to constitute his one sure proof that he is different from everyone else. There are interesting trends in the recognition that these drives of the sexual urge are to be sublimated rather than repressed.[17]

By eight or nine the child begins to transfer some of the burdens of this problem to certain formal institutions (e.g., the Church becomes what is good, Wall Street what is bad). During these early years it is difficult to decide how much of this mirrors the remarks of adults and how much originates with the child. It probably starts with the former and subtly changes to the latter. His attitude is affected by the extent to which he realizes that the institutional structure is what human beings make it—not permanent and inviolable in itself.[18]

This impersonalization of the problem of guilt and difference is apparently an "efficiency mechanism," similar to that of the wall of status preservation,[19] which also uses symbolization. Once this transfer has started, it is easily carried to the point where it meets all the youngster's problems of individual development. "It is the Church that makes me good." "It is the rigidity of the school's demands that makes me appear an academic failure." When the mechanism reaches this stage, we begin to realize what a large part of the personal load is thus taken over by institutional structure and to see that the trends towards an individual-cen-

17 S. H. Britt, *Social Psychology of Modern Life* (New York, Farrar, 1941), Chapter XIII. This also has a pretty good bibliography.
18 E.g., *Trends*, pp. 382–402.   19 Chapter 3.

tered culture[20] that imply denial of the God-given place of institutions are placing new and heavy weights upon the personality.

But just as each child feels—and has the need to feel—that he is
different from any other, he must also feel that his family differs
in some intimate way from the Family—that it is more quarrel-
some or more jealous than a family should be. Here once more
the feeling of guilt becomes inextricably mingled with that of
difference—and therefore quite as hard to do away with. Thus
the "efficiency mechanism" of transferring the problems of good
and evil to the institutional structure in the end intensifies the
problem, as it brings the matter of individuality even more
acutely to the fore.

No new aspects of the problem discussed in this chapter emerge
during adolescence, but the child's reactions may be intensified;
for, as so frequently pointed out in the following pages, all the
issues that he meets are sharpened and magnified during this
period. Special mention should perhaps be made here of the frequent appearance in schizophrenics of reactions seemingly dependent on feelings of guilt. The withdrawal, the diffuse depression, the development of rituals which seem to offer atonement—
these all indicate that the patient feels he is irrevocably set apart
from others, is the perpetrator of some not-to-be-forgiven sin.

We might stop here, but for two aspects of the dual problem of
the feeling of difference and of guilt which do not develop until
after adolescence. But as they work their way out they affect
younger members of the family and throw considerable light on
the insistence of the problem as a whole. One of these aspects
appears in the progress of courtship, when such questions as
"Will she find out?" "Will she still care?" "Should I tell her?"
are apt to intrude.

20 Plant, pp. 405–413.

There are at least four important factors in the individual's reactions to this. (1) Where the relation of intimacy occurs in a cultural pattern dominated by romanticism, there is a compulsion to frankness between the persons involved, though experience has long since persuaded the individual that he can't tell anyone all about himself. This would destroy the sense of difference, of individuality. His reserve is partly justified by the feeling that what he has kept to himself is the "bad" part, and so once more the feelings of difference and guilt naturally strengthen each other. (2) The whole matter is further mixed up with the development of many of the other problems under discussion in this book. For instance, security considerations,[21] which are so pressing in the matter of marriage, may either forbid the telling of certain things or as insistently demand it. If one has carried a secret hatred of his sister to this point, should he or should he not divulge his guilt as a final test of the love and belongingness he craves? (3) A decision either way obviously sets up a hazard not only for the courtship but for the wedded life to follow. (4) The source of the feeling of guilt—the sense of difference that sets the individual apart—may seem a mere nothing to everyone else. It is for this reason that the psychiatrist is frequently amazed at the picayune bases of his patients' feelings of guilt and just as amazed at his own inability to clear them up. It is at least possible that this explains some of the more bizarre interpretations one reads. Many a "history" would be a sorry affair if it recorded what the patient feels guilty and disturbed about—but this is never the case by the time the resourceful psychiatrist has pictured what is "undoubtedly symbolized."

In the choice of a mate, whether one looks for a person who isn't "at all like" himself or is "just like" himself, it is evident that the feeling of guilt or difference is showing its hand. Here, again, a projection phenomenon must be involved, as there are very few

[21] Chapter 1.

courtships in which the lovers' knowledge ever goes beyond what
each thinks the other to be. Thus the period is one of peculiar
freedom for each to project upon the other the desired or hoped
for traits.[22] Highly personalized as these problems are, it seems
obvious to me that they are sharply affected by trends in communication and transportation, which largely govern courtship opportunities.[23]

The other aspect appears in family life when there is the projection on the children of all of the as-yet-unsolved problems that
have appeared in this chapter. This shows itself in two somewhat
distinct ways. (1) There is the need of feeling that each family is
different from the Family.[24] This means a constant pressure to
find or invent differences or deficiencies in the children. One day
posterity will look with amusement upon our bright efforts at
giving reassurance on this or that peculiarity in the child, when
reassurance is almost the last thing the parent can accept. I do
not mean that we should condone the tendency of some parents to
magnify the small missteps of their children, but that we should
try to understand this, and to see that we cannot do away with it
unless we give the parents some other less damaging way of satisfying the need for difference. (2) Then there is the fear that the
child will develop the very behavior or trait about which the
parent has a feeling of guilt, with the result that he may be un-
reasonably severe in criticism of what others recognize as his own
outstanding fault.[25] There is the added difficulty that the wall of

[22] Perhaps marriage is one's first real experience with the problem of tolerance
—of accepting people for what they are rather than for what we wished them to
be or thought them to be. We see many who in the first two or three years of marriage must strive for a continuance of the projected images of courtship or give up
in disgust. It is common in a clinic such as ours to meet people who know the
whole grand ritual of racial or national problems of tolerance—but who outdo
the world's most insistent bigot as to husband or wife or child. We should have a
much better world if everyone would begin these nice reforms at home.

[23] *Trends,* pp. 168–203.   [24] See above and Plant, pp. 165–167.

[25] It makes one's flesh creep to hear (as one often does), "He's a fine one to criti-
cize his boy for selfishness—he's the most selfish person I know." It is so often that
here lies precisely the reason that the father *must* be critical!

status preservation[26] keeps the parent from admitting that he has this particular trait—not to mention that he is in any way worried about it.[27]

[26] Chapter 3.

[27] The inheritance of various traits is still shrouded in mystery. Something of what we actually know is summarized in C. E. Keeler, "Genetics and the Heredity of Mental Disease," in *Mental Health*, edited by F. R. Moulton and P. O. Komora (Lancaster, American Association for the Advancement of Science, 1939), p. 71.

CHAPTER 5

Symbolization and Reality

We see children who have the dual problem of adjusting themselves to the fact that life is largely made up of symbols, while maintaining a fairly clear distinction between them and the realities for which they stand. In fact, the ability to use symbols—to generalize experience—is the measuring rod of the most widely used scales for the evaluation of what we call intelligence,[1] and usually begins early in the life of each individual. Later on, the omnipresence of symbols in all the social relationships of our culture forces him to make a constant effort at keeping some sort of balance between an increasing dependence upon symbols as a means of communication and an increasing tendency to endow them with reality.

The latter aspect of the problem—present in almost every moment of one's life—never becomes evident in a way that the individual can actually grasp it, come to grips with it. Perhaps no other question so taunts us with its will-o'-the-wisp elusiveness, for though reality itself is made up of a series of disparate, idiomatic experiences, these separate phenomena are necessarily distorted in the process of generalization and the use of symbols by means of which generalization is expressed. But generalization is necessary; we could not live together in such complexity without it.[2]

It is therefore not a matter of chance that Pareto[3] puts this

[1] Chapter 15.

[2] Probably no one could even live alone without this constant yen to develop symbols (words, for instance) for experiences, but that isn't important now.

[3] A full discussion of the relation of the formulations of the present work to those of Pareto will be found in the Appendix.

problem under his Class I residues (instinct for combinations), and that he gives it major emphasis throughout his last three volumes. In Pareto's view the instinct to make combinations "reaches out" towards the disparate phenomena and rationalizes the gap between what it "wants" and what it actually "gets."

There are times when the individual is free of this problem, giving himself up to the sadness or exhilaration of the moment with no thought of past or future, with no need to compare. Perhaps this is one of the important factors in the part that the sexual act plays in our lives—here, for once, is an idiomatic experience with no demand for tie to what has been or will be.[4]

For the most part, however, we go through life trying to construct symbols, even though we can't do this without destroying precisely the things we are trying to preserve. As a relative matter the use of symbols increases with age, and one of the great sources of family difficulty is that parents impose symbols on children who have not had adequate experience to understand them. For instance, as the four-year-old dawdles—and continues to dawdle—we say "Hurry." We say it again and are amazed when the child replies in simple fashion, "I *am* hurrying." The word "danger" is another symbol we have built out of realities. We say to the child that such and such is "dangerous" and pretty much resent his inability to understand us.

It may have appeared that I should be happy if we could do away with these symbols.[5] Nothing is further from the truth. I not only understand the compelling need of generalization but recognize man's constant urge to erect symbols. These are necessary conservers of energy.[6] What disturbs me is the speed with

---

[4] Obviously the term "sexual act" is used here in the sense that it is in Chapter 9 (the physical urge) rather than in Chapter 10 (its language values).

[5] Plant, pp. 408–409; throughout the book there are many other references to the distortion of reality that is involved in the process of symbolization.

[6] This point is well developed in Andras Angyal's book, *Foundations for a Science of Personality* (New York, Commonwealth Fund, 1941)—particularly in Chap-

which symbols have recently been created. The printing press has very rapidly raised the value of the word, and in the last hundred years we have seen that money similarly has usurped the place of the things for which it stands.[7] Today curricular techniques, grades, marks—all these have been endowed with reality. The two great dangers (and we are now well ensnared in both) are that the child learns the symbol before he has had the experience which should be its basis, and that the symbol becomes endowed with the reality for which it earlier stood.[8]

One matter appears[9] upon which, surprising as it may seem, no work has been done by those who should be most interested. Up to the present time the schools have been primarily interested in the child's ability to work with symbols (words, numbers, etc.), but have done nothing about the child's introduction to the corresponding type of mental experience. Schools that have developed summer round-ups to assure healthy bodies and every conceivable immunization, seem to take it for granted that some heaven-sent guardian has watched over the child as he has taken his first steps in the symbolic thinking so important to his school progress. This is not so much a plea for school oversight of the baby's first use of words as a prediction that, one of these days, sensitive antennae from the school will discover that in

ter III. The author tends to place the distortion in what I call the envelope, where undoubtedly *some* of it does occur.

7 Thus one hopes that the huge mass of gold buried in Kentucky may come again to life (coldness increases the heaviness of its hand); thus one fears that this very revival might be in terms of the earlier phenomena that gave of their life to that gold, rather than in terms of the events and meanings of the day of resurrection.

8 This is only half of the story, as students of semantics know full well. The very lifelessness of the symbol increases its inertia. What a motley crew rallied during the war to the banner of "the Western Democracies"—how much of the tragedy of each one's life comes from vain effort at fitting in today's events to words or formulae built so vivaciously only a brief time ago!

Obviously these paragraphs are the feeblest sort of expression of part of Korzybski's monumental work on general semantics. It is too bad that so important a contribution is veiled in such intricate and difficult modes of expression. The reference is Alfred Korzybski, *Science and Sanity* (Lancaster, Science Press, 1933).

9 See pp. 71 f.

those youthful days lies the answer to a great many educational problems.[10]

Once the child has entered upon his academic career, reading, arithmetic, the social sciences, literature, and so forth, vie with each other in presenting symbols before he has experienced the realities upon which they are based.[11] No wonder that most students "re-cite" their lessons, that they toss back these empty containers with which they are pelted! One hopes for the time when the group which talks so much about "education for democracy" will not continue in a rigidly authoritarian set-up merely to give so much data about democracy.

The earliest practical contact we have with the child in the problem of symbolization is in the matter of his "talking." It is true that there are earlier generalizations, as in his averaging all the things his mother does into a pleasing symbol and in reacting appropriately to that symbol. However, this is not a feasible point at which to study the child's power of generalization. If he could draw or finger-paint or otherwise express symbols before talking, we should have more reliable criteria. The current trends towards word-centered forms of education increase parental pressures towards early talking,[12] with the result that we often see stammering and other forms of taut nervous tension in children who are urged to talk too soon and with too adult a vocabulary. Occasionally such children are slow, meticulous talkers—almost elephantine in the measured, lumbering mode of their speech. But we usually find the other picture.

[10] Indeed, it may be that many of the non-readers, reading-disability cases, or even "intellectually retarded" children, are really only those who have taken incorrect steps in the early matter of developing and using symbols in their handling of reality.

[11] See M. Semmelmeyer, *Evaluation of the Application of General Semantics Methodology in a "Reading Readiness" Program*, The Second American Congress on General Semantics (Chicago, Institute of General Semantics, 1943), pp. 529-540.

[12] Prescott, p. 121.

As speech really gets under way—at two or three years—it makes a difference whether the child is chiefly communicating with those who are older or with others of his own age. If the siblings who "teach" the child to talk are only slightly older, he makes efforts to reach up to them, and once more we get a picture of nervous tension which results in stammering. On the other hand, if the siblings are considerably older or the parents are the "teachers," it is more frequent to find the child continuing baby talk for an undue time (a condition that is rapidly cleared up as he goes to nursery school). The trends of importance are those in the size of families and spacing of siblings,[13] and those in the development of nursery schools where children play with their peers.[14]

As the child gets to school age he meets squarely the word-centered emphasis of the curriculum. Here, once more, stammering appears if the school demands are a little ahead of the child's development and baby talk persists if these demands are so far ahead that he is invited back into a dependent relationship. Here, too, appears that host of reading disabilities which we see so much of today. The important trends are those in delaying the curricular demands in reading and those in establishing the time when reading changes from a subject to a tool.[15]

The problem is complicated by the tendency of the school to develop word symbols ahead of experiences which would give them meaning. Precisely the same problem exists with regard to numbers, so that we are also interested in trends towards delaying the teaching of arithmetic.[16] One fairly common experience will

[13] *Trends,* pp. 680–684.
[14] *Trends,* p. 788. But completely out-dated by the war which has seen an enormous increase in such facilities. It seems a fair guess that more and more children will go to nursery school particularly if the curriculum is fitted into (instead of stealing the thunder of) the kindergarten.
[15] National Society for the Study of Education, *36th Yearbook, Part I* (Bloomington Public School Publishing Co., 1937). Chapters I and III are very enlightening, but for those who must hurry the exact references are pp. 6–9 and 49–61.
[16] I am sure that children should have muscular experiences with the relation-

suffice for example. Many children who have a great deal of trouble with arithmetic have little trouble with algebra (i.e., they are then old enough to have had adequate experience with the realities for which the algebraic symbols stand). In the language field the important trends are those in demands upon children in regard to reading[17] and in vocabulary demands in school.[18]

Finally the child is pressed by the requirements of our social system to spend an increasing amount of time in word-centered schools. Those of nonacademic frame of mind rebel at school demands, play truant, or run into delinquency of every sort as a compensation for their failures in this situation. There are interesting trends here in the development of vocational types of education,[19] in society's willingness to accept the validity of nonacademic education,[20] and in measuring school achievement in terms of nonacademic rather than academic standards.[21]

The child's struggle to determine how much reality he should bestow upon the symbol itself usually begins when he is about seven, but it may appear sooner. Perhaps it is only sharpened by what seems to be its originator—the school experience, where, as early as the first grade, marks and promotion assume more importance for both the child and his parents than the progress for which they stand. When the use of these symbols makes the child

ship of distances and quantities as a basis for adding, subtracting, and multiplying. One school which has been using blocks instead of flash-cards reports after three years that the children learn more slowly but are extremely accurate as to answers. It looks as though a real feeling for numerical combinations had been substituted for reliance on memory. See also *Tentative Course of Study for Virginia Elementary Schools* (Richmond, State Board of Education, 1934).

17 *Trends*, p. 335. See also National Society for the Study of Education, *op. cit.*, pp. 23–44.

18 *Ibid.* All of Chapter IX is good, but see particularly pp. 279–287.

19 *Trends*, p. 677.

20 *Trends*, p. 677. Note how dramatically the early 1940's have reversed an earlier trend. How long this will last after a war that has put a premium on this sort of education no one knows.

21 Prescott, p. 247.

aware that he is different from the others, his reactions are those
of inferiority.[22] The matter is complicated by the difficulty of
separating the child's own sense of failure from that caught as a
result of parental upset.[23] When the sense of failure is a matter of
contagion, it's perfectly possible to have panicky pictures of insecurity in the youngster.[24] The important trends here are those
in doing away with "marks" in school and in passing children
along to higher grades regardless of their academic accomplishment[25]—and those in removing competitive subjects from the
lower grades, so that the emphasis will be on human relationships.[26]

By the age of ten many children are affected by symbols to such
an extent that everything they read or study or are interested in
is dictated by what is required in school (i.e., by the marks they
wish to get). Many of the problems of poor school work originate
here—the school curriculum not happening to provide something
that the child is interested in, the child not having as yet learned
to work at anything that does not contribute to better marks or
"passing his grade." Trends in the amounts of material demanded
by school curricula are therefore important.[27]

Also by ten the child has learned to measure success and happiness in terms of size of residence, possessions, and so forth.[28] So

22 Chapter 14.
23 To the extent that it is parental—the "failure" itself is sharpened by the fact
that the adult is so much more accustomed (than is the child) to measuring life in
terms of symbols.
24 For what it is worth I may report that it is a growing procedure in our area to
retard children a grade only after his parents are thoroughly in agreement with
the wisdom of that step. We think that we have adequate data that such retardation does not disturb the child beyond the first two or three weeks of the next
fall term. Regardless of other considerations some schools will not retard children
without this parental understanding and acceptance.
25 New York State Regents' Inquiry, *Education for American Life: A New Program for the State of New York* (New York, McGraw-Hill, 1938), p. 50.
26 Prescott, p. 247.   27 *Trends*, pp. 329–338.
28 I have suspected that this aspect of the problem appears later in rural areas
than in suburban areas but have no proof. In suburban areas the rapid shift of
population means that the "place" of a family tends much more to rest on various possessions than is the case (rural) where the family is known as such or is the

one finds tendencies to steal (where the stolen material is given away to buy social favor), to aggrandizement through tall tales and other such compensating behavior. Trends in population movements,[29] in suburban developments,[30] and in economic fluctuations[31] are all significant here.

I don't know when it is that the influence of the school experience begins to spread to the other aspects of success and failure. However, the child soon begins to think of people in terms of various feats (Babe Ruth is a certain number of home runs, etc.), so that trends in specialization in business, profession, or sport are important.[32] By adolescence this problem of the endowment of the symbol with reality appears in the matter of money.

The use of various symbols to carry personal loads appears somewhat later than the age of ten. The following considerations, at least, are involved: (1) What loads can be transferred to these symbols? This is discussed in Chapters 1 and 3, and, indeed, throughout the book there are numerous references to situations in which a child may use money or fanciful tales to carry the load of his need for a place, for success. (2) Is the symbol an adequate carrier of the load? An illustration of the constant, nagging character of this question appears in the shy or frustrated child who tries to effect an escape by getting outstanding marks in school, always having to press towards higher marks because of the feeling that what he has attained is not sufficient to hide his problem.[33] So much of what we ordinarily call overcompensation has

case (urban) where the very crowding of the population lessens the need and acuteness of personal or family competition.

[29] High mobility of population again throws a heavy burden upon material possessions and show, as means of establishing family position. *Trends*, pp. 8–17.

[30] *Trends*, pp. 14–15, 461–467.   [31] *Trends*, Chapter v.

[32] *Trends*, pp. 342–343. Also New York State Regents' Inquiry (*op. cit.*), pp. 15, 26–28.

[33] There is an excellent discussion of this matter (with case material) by Ruth L. Munroe in *Teaching the Individual*, Sarah Lawrence College Publications, no. 3 (New York, Columbia University Press, 1942), Chapters vii and viii.

its origin here. (3) How treacherous is the symbol? Its very imper-sonality means that it is much more under the control of social trends than of the individual. One sees this in the distress that besets children when a depression cuts down on their clothing,[34] or in their happiness when good times make it possible for the family to own two cars instead of one.[35] (4) How far can symbols (particularly verbal ones) actually hide emotional problems? I am sure that this becomes less of a question with the years—that for children the telltale psychomotor tensions are less easily hid-den behind camouflaging symbols than is the case for adults. In fact, on occasion one sees a teacher, whom he knows to be very much disturbed emotionally, do a very fair job in the classroom as long as she can make the experience a word-centered, formal, academic affair. This particular example raises two pretty dis-turbing questions. The first is what we do to such teachers when we ask them to *live* with their children in the classroom.[36] The second is whether the teacher can ever really believe that chil-dren bring their own emotional problems to the classroom when she herself is quite able (or seems to be) to keep these out of the curriculum.

As the individual grows older, his effort to express emotional experiences by means of symbols becomes more constant (one sees this beginning in early adolescence). But as such experiences are unique, idiomatic, and not subject to generalization, symbols are inadequate for expressing the phenomena and relationships

[34] This is far more important to junior and senior high school children than to younger ones. The latter have little difficulty in exhibiting worn soles to their teachers, while their older siblings hide such matters with every sort of device.

[35] On the effect of social and economic changes and of their rate of acceleration see *Trends*, pp. xi–lxx, particularly p. xii, and Chapter v. The latter is long read-ing, but the subject is complex and I know no better or more authoritative pic-ture of its complexities.

[36] This is a question which the modern educator has often side-stepped—the matter of how many teachers can afford to cast off the protective armor of tables, spelling, recitative procedures.

involved.[37] Furthermore, the emotions which symbols arouse in others are unpredictable. Nevertheless, with all these difficulties, the average person continues through life to try to express his emotional experiences in words or other symbols.

This leads to many odd situations. (1) We constantly attempt to tell others of beautiful or impressive experiences, even though we frequently give up with an exasperated "Oh, I can't really put it into words." (2) Because we know that the emotions are really expressed in the psychomotor tensions, we have adopted certain exaggerated (even grotesque) attitudes and physical expressions as fairly satisfactory symbols of the emotional experiences involved. (3) In the field of sexual relationships, for example, there have been many efforts to enrich the content by publicizing the actions of satisfactory experiences.[38] (4) There have been various efforts to *teach* the emotional life to others, without taking into consideration that emotions are transmitted by contagion, and many people have been fooled by books into believing that courage can be taught timidly and tolerance intolerantly.[39] (5) It is the baffling experience of each one of us that, no matter how often we try and what symbols we use, we can't recapture an emotional experience, can't relive it. (6) In both prose and poetry, but more notably in poetry, there have been recent efforts to convey emotion directly by sound, the intellectual content of the words being hidden or purposely distorted.

A special aspect of this problem appears in adolescence (and, of

[37] This does not strictly apply in the field of intellectual phenomena, where symbols are adequate and useful as long as we understand their relationship to the things for which they stand. The reader who objects to the summary way in which I divide matters into "emotional" and "intellectual" may be somewhat reassured by my acknowledgment that the distinction is one of preponderant rather than of absolute values, which have been adopted to simplify the exposition.

[38] Plant, p. 225.

[39] *Intercultural Education in American Schools; Proposed Objectives and Methods* by W. E. Vickery and S. G. Cole (New York, Harper, 1943), devotes only one sentence in 200 pages to the importance of the attitude of those operating the program.

course, later becomes very marked) as the individual sees more and more clearly that he has to use symbols in communicating with others at the same time that he sees how essentially inaccurate these are. So as the child grows older, one often hears, "I must try to tell you, but I know that I can't put it into words." Or one recognizes the same thing in the child's attitude about going to church and his conflict over stopping church attendance—"I'm religious, but in going to church I'm not expressing *my* religion."[40] The same thing appears in the frequently heard "He isn't much on book-learning, but I would call him a highly intelligent man."[41]

And the dilemma runs its course through some of our most perplexing problems—that we set up various institutions to symbolize and feed our emotional needs, only to find that this very crystallization is itself the factor that prevents the adequate expression of the need.[42] So we see institutions built—to crumble—and ask ourselves whether there can ever be life and power in anything beyond the experience of building. Once the institution becomes the symbol—from that moment, perchance, it is doomed.[43]

[40] Peter Blos, *The Adolescent Personality* (New York, Appleton-Century, 1941), pp. 296–298.

[41] A somewhat different but brilliantly helpful approach to this same problem appears in Elton Mayo's *Social Problems of an Industrial Civilization* (Cambridge, Harvard University Press, 1945). Page 16 gives the idea, but the whole book is more than worth reading. The author's constant stress on the point that symbols *seem* such easy ways of communicating is of basic importance.

[42] Plant, pp. 234 ff.

[43] For this in relation to the family or the Church, see *Trends,* p. xiv.

CHAPTER 6

Cadence

We see children who have the problem of adjusting their own rate of ripening or maturing to the rates of others with whom they come in contact or live, and to the rather fixed and predetermined rates of the various social groups or institutions of which they are a part. This concept of individual rates of growth is well known in the physical and intellectual fields, and fairly adequate measuring scales exist. It is my own guess that the rate of maturation is a practical and valid concept in the emotional field, though adequate standardized tests for this have not been devised. The clinical pictures involved here are of an entirely negative kind. That is, it is difficult to describe the sort of person whose cadence is being properly met by the rates of those about him. But one can easily recognize the child who is being asked (or rather is asking himself) to speed up his cadence; here the picture is one of tenseness, shown in stammering, enuresis, hypertonicity, fatigue, and so forth. And quite as easily one can recognize the child of whom a slower cadence is asked—the restless one who "doesn't have enough to do," the lazy, inattentive one, or the one constantly in petty mischief.

While a great deal has been done by way of setting up rates of physical development and while there has even been recognition of individual differences in the rates of development of both primary and secondary sex characters,[1] very few attempts have been made to determine whether a certain rate of maturation in one aspect of the physical field holds for the other indices of develop-

[1] J. P. C. Griffith and A. G. Mitchell, *Textbook of Pediatrics* (Philadelphia, Saunders, 1941), pp. 2-22.

ment.[2] One does not doubt that a few children with very slow maturation in one area show the same in other areas, but questions whether this is true for the "usual" child. And there is a second, quite as important, matter about which we know as little. If we discover the rate of ripening at four, can we predict anything about the rate at fourteen or twenty-four?

Obviously the so-called intelligence tests reveal a rate of ripening in that particular field. The relative constancy of the I.Q. seems to answer the latter of the above questions. However, except for Terman's work with genius,[3] no attempt has been made to establish a parallel between the rate of maturation in the intellectual field and those in the physical and emotional fields.[4] Moreover, a further difficulty arises from the spacing of the individual intelligence tests, which are allocated in such a way as to make the I.Q. appear constant. By way of comparison, it may be noted that the clinician gets an entirely different picture in working with children (or watching nations)—that of uneven growth. Our patients show spurts of growth and then periods of solidifying gains.[5]

But what of maturation in the emotional areas and in those of social and personal adjustment? Obviously, in discussing the problems of this book I have assumed that each individual has a relatively fixed rate of ripening, though I have no proof of it—in any objective, measurable sense. I do feel sure, however, that the rate with which I and my patient move towards a goal is quite as important as the goal itself. Further, I have the impression that

[2] *Trends,* pp. 794 ff.; and Young, p. 373. However, see M. E. Breckenridge and E. L. Vincent, *Child Development* (Philadelphia, Saunders, 1943), pp. 33-47.

[3] Lewis M. Terman and others, *Genetic Studies of Genius,* vol. 1: *Mental and Physical Traits of a Thousand Gifted Children* (Stanford University Press, 1925). This work tends to give a positive answer to this question.

[4] Editor's note: Such studies of child development as that of the Child Research Council at the University of Colorado are currently accumulating data which will throw light on this question.

[5] The only group in which this is frequently a measurable (and indeed dramatic) affair is that of Mongolian idiots, where sudden short periods of startling growth in the intellectual field are clinically well known.

there is a certain consistency to this rate—that if the child's superego develops slowly in relation to property rights, it also develops
slowly in relation to the give and take of play life. This is said in
full recognition that the "rate" is not constant, that its consistency
probably includes alternating periods of rest and growth.[6] Moreover, I feel sure (admittedly without measurable proof) that the
rate of progress in such matters is not highly correlated with the
I.Q. or with the rate of physical development.

None of these uncertainties invalidates what appears in the re-
mainder of this chapter. It still remains true that the rate at which
a given child arrives at a given adjustment goal often differs from
the expected or hoped-for rate. In this connection, it would not
be surprising to find one bright morning that children had been
nailed to a new cross—that of the Adjustment Quotient. My own
work in some dim way implies that this exists, but I hope it will
be made to serve rather than to dominate, if it ever becomes generally recognized.

In spite of its importance, those who deal with children often
give short shrift to this matter. For the school this is not a fair
statement: the difficulty there has been an overweening interest
in the cadence of just one small part of the child's personality—his
academic or formal intelligence. The more recent decision on the
part of many schools to make placement on the basis of chronological age rather than mental age represents a forward step but
does not meet the real problem. One guesses that unless educators soon find a cadence that underlies the physical, intellectual,
emotional, and adjustment aspects, they will develop a number of
these quotients for each child and make that adjustment which
seems to do the least harm.

Though clinically we know fairly well when we are going too

---

[6] This is something like the discussion of the speed with which different types of
trains go from one metropolis to another—the time for the trip is consistent for
each type of train though the rate of speed (stops for this or that, stretches for
speeding, etc.) is not constant.

fast or too slow, a more accurate timing must remain for the present on a trial-and-error basis. It is probably true, on the one hand,
that many therapeutic programs succeed in spite of wrong timing
(the goal in view being more important than certain faults of cadence); and, on the other, that success is sometimes due to the patient's feeling that the program is in adjustment with his own cadence rather than to his desire to attain a somewhat indefinite
goal.[7]

Anyone who approaches this problem from a neurological direction is of course intrigued by the importance of the maturation of the nerve fibres. It is most inviting to assume that in some
subtle way a time schedule for changes in the nerves is involved
in any adjustment. But if the existence of such a time schedule
could be established, at present we should have no means of measuring it.

It is my own feeling that the average child does a considerable
amount of jockeying for the first few years, and does not settle
into his cadence until he is about six. Certainly we see some children who start out with extremely rapid development, to settle
into a more average growth later, and others who seem to be "slow
starters"—gathering speed from four or five on. The latter phenomenon appears quite dramatically in prematurely born children, who may take as long as three to find their real rate of development.

Consequently during these early years there are sharp pressures
on the child as he differs from what is expected of him each month
—the slow child anxiously urged on, the accelerated child happily
cheered to further acceleration. Here one sees pictures of strain
and irritability, which are of course largely "secondary" in the

---

[7] Clear and detailed pictures of this appear in F. H. Allen, *Psychotherapy with
Children* (New York, Norton, 1942), particularly Chapters iii–ix.

sense that the parents are the ones who worry and the child simply senses that something is wrong. All the trends in developing scales to measure the growth of young children have a general bearing on this matter.[8]

The problem of adjustment to the cadence demands of other members of the family begins in the first few months of the child's life. Here the picture is the same as above—the tenseness later showing in stammering, enuresis, or other symptoms of a child trying to overreach himself. The important trends are those in size of families (in small families there is a greater hazard that the parents will impose their own cadence on the child)[9] and in the spacing of siblings.[10]

Closely allied to the problem of adjustment within the family is that of meeting the cadence demands of the neighborhood. In view of the tendency, as families crowd together, to measure position by the accomplishments of the various individuals, trends in population concentration must be taken into account.[11]

As we come to the close of the first six-year period the problems remain very much the same as those discussed in the previous section, except for changes in emphasis, as difficulties arise less in relation to the child's own rate of growth and more in relation to the rate expected by his parents or established by siblings and neighbors. The child's diffuse irritability now centers in nervous habits. Tendencies to bully, acts of revenge against the ones who are setting the pace, or sharp withdrawals from any sort of group

[8] A. G. Mitchell, "Pediatric Bibliography," *Monograph of the Society for Research in Child Development,* vol. 6, serial no. 27, no. 1, pp. 1–3 (Washington, the Society and the National Research Council, 1941); also Max Seham and Grete Seham, *The Tired Child* (Philadelphia, Lippincott, 1926), pp. 3–16.

[9] *Trends,* pp. 681–685.

[10] Mildred Parten, "A Statistical Analysis of the Modern Family," *Annals of the American Academy of Political and Social Science,* vol. 160, pp. 29–37, particularly p. 34, March 1932.

[11] *Trends,* pp. 1–17.

play are also manifested.[12] The trends affecting the earlier years are still important, though the situation is now affected by certain new elements: the disappearance of the clan family or great family,[13] placement of children in nursery school,[14] and the extent of the roaming range.[15] Data on trends in the heterogeneity of neighborhoods would be of the greatest interest.

The problem of cadence is next met in the standardization of the school. At five or six the child encounters what is perhaps as class conscious a cultural pattern as has ever been seen. Here each child's progress is measured by all the rest in months as well as years. On the day he enters his exact age and accomplishments are pretty well known throughout the whole group. A very efficient envelope is therefore needed to protect him from the scorn or awed amazement of what has become almost his entire world.[16] Perhaps the best indication we have of the encompassing nature of the school environment is that fact that when children realize they are not meeting the cadence of the school, their responses run the gamut of conduct disorders a clinician sees. The list is too long to give in full, but one particular response may be singled out here as illustrative of the kind of complication involved. This is the sad plight of the quiet and polite child who floats along through the grades, never really fitting into the curricular demands of the school, never rebelling enough to bring himself to the attention of the teacher. Such a child is usually referred to us at the time of a reshuffle, when he changes school or goes to junior high school. Suddenly he begins to show his rebellion by truancy

[12] This is often a source of traumatic introversion (Plant, pp. 111–113).
[13] *Trends*, pp. 672–673.
[14] *Trends*, p. 788. Note how the war has out-dated the earlier statements.
[15] *Trends*, pp. 172–181. There are considerable data as to the effect of various means of transportation on this roaming range. What we should like data on is the effect of urbanization on the number and distribution of the child's friends.
[16] See pp. 72 f.

or other misconduct, to the surprised horror of all who have known him as a conformist. Then it is discovered that there has long been a serious dislocation between the child's actual growth and the school's demands. The trends to be noted are those in the rigidity of requirements for promotion,[17] those in dispensing with grades,[18] and those in grading on other bases than i.q.'s or academic achievement.[19]

The child meets the stratification of recreational activities when he is about eight (though it begins to seem as if there were trends towards an earlier age of first encounter). As in the educational area, his reactions to failure include every sort of escape, substitutive, and regressive behavior. But as the element of compulsion which is inseparable from the school situation is lacking here, there is a shift towards neuroses that keep the youngster out of activities that press upon him. Sometimes, this same absence of compulsion serves to blur the whole symptom picture. That is, an interest in a hobby at home may mask the youngster's inability to meet the neighborhood pattern. The demand that he go to a school and be in a certain grade at twelve has no such positive escape.

There are two roughly discernible areas of recreational pressure. That of the first is exerted in innumerable informal ways: "Have you seen this movie?" "Do you listen to such and such a radio program?" A rapid stratification is developing in these and allied fields. Woe to the clinician who asks the child about a certain radio program six months beyond the age dictated by his neighborhood as the upper limit at which it is proper to listen! This problem, like all the others under discussion, stretches up into adult life, rigorously demanding that such and such an ac-

[17] New York State Regents' Inquiry, *Education for American Life: A New Program for the State of New York* (New York, McGraw-Hill, 1938), pp. 47–51.
[18] Prescott, p. 247.　　[19] Prescott, p. 234.

tivity or recreation be taken up at a stated time. There are interesting and compelling trends in advertising the propriety or smartness of various forms of recreation[20] and in using such activities as means of proclaiming social position.[21]

The other area is closely allied to the first. Pressure is exerted through various national organizations with character-building programs for children. Trends in the actual growth of such groups are important,[22] as are those in the standardization of their programs.

The development of the junior high school reflects a special aspect of the cadence of sexual maturation. The school's expectancy that the psychological changes of adolescence will occur at the age of twelve makes for much simplification in adjustment for all except those who do not so mature at just that age! The reactions of inferiority and shyness, of feeling "out of the group," are sharply intensified by the narcissism and vulnerability of this period. Some of the trends to be noted here are those in the development of substitution of a 6–3–3 grade system for an 8–4 grade system,[23] those in school attendance above the sixth grade,[24] those in making high school and college attendance a badge of social rather than academic achievement,[25] and those forcing children to stay in the stratified school set-up through shutting the labor market to them.[26]

A few years later the problem acquires a new stress because the school makes no allowance in its curriculum or class placement for the sharp difference in cadence in the two sexes. Girls mature much more rapidly than boys, and at fourteen or fifteen may begin to have their social life with boys who are two or three years

[20] *Trends*, pp. 208–214, Chapter xviii.   [21] As in golf, *Trends*, p. 927.
[22] *Trends*, pp. 945, 1039.   [23] *Trends*, pp. 337–338.
[24] *Trends*, p. 328.   [25] Prescott, pp. 208–209.
[26] *Trends*, p. 327.

older, while continuing to attend class and compete academically with boys of their own age.[27]

A host of new standardizations appear throughout this adolescent period—as in clothes. These make short shrift of individuality and of individual rates of maturing and adjustment. Trends in the speed and imperiousness of new styles are important.[28] Where the envelope cannot sufficiently protect the child from the fact that these social cadences are different from his own, we tend to see withdrawal or quiet expressions of inferiority.[29] Overcompensating reactions appear, but in our experience they are uncommon.

We have very little data about one very important aspect of this problem—the "tempo of life." If there is any indication today of earlier physical and emotional maturing, certainly the age at which it dramatically shows itself is that of early adolescence through trends in "staying up late," in going to dances, and in doing this or that with the opposite sex. It is a hard problem to get at from the behavior of the children themselves, who become aware of it through parental disturbance over the change in cadence—the change in the speed with which people grow up. It is therefore complicated by parent-child authority relationships[30] —in fact children invariably discuss it with us as an authority problem rather than as a cadence problem.

The only trends that are measurable in this area are those in

27 During the war we saw a sharp increase in sex delinquency in older adolescent girls. There were many intricate contributing factors.
28 *Trends*, pp. 877–880. Note, for instance, the disappearance of homemade clothes.
29 Junior and senior high school teachers so often report that they "never hear" their children complain of not having the things other children have. See Plant, pp. 206–207.
30 Chapter 2.

prolonging adolescence[31] by withholding adult duties and responsibilities. The children's responses to this include many different kinds of reactions: leaving school to get any sort of job,[32] running away from home in search of responsibility, and developing a progressive avoidance of responsibility.

In my own thinking I make a separate section of the difficulties arising from marked differences in the development of the secondary sex characters. These could be woven into the other sections of the present chapter, but they stand out quite separately for the child. Here we deal with normal variations in the appearance of the genitalia or the typical fat deposits, in voice changes, in menstruation. There are important trends here in sex education and in knowledge of the wide individual differences in sex development.[33] The child's response to variations may take the form of boisterous overcompensation, but we usually find anxiety states—worry, preoccupation, and so forth.

Here our clinical experience stops, though I can't resist mentioning a few of the dramatic problems of cadence which show themselves in adult life. Of course, none of those we have outlined ceases its reverberations, but several new ones appear, including the disturbing and exciting problem of differences in cadence between husband and wife. Trends in the marriage age are interesting,[34] as are those in "acceptable" modes of meeting the sexual urge previous to marriage.[35] Then there is that host of

[31] I have used the term in its sociological rather than its biological sense. *Trends,* pp. 227, 303.

[32] The marked shortening of sociological adolescence brought about by the war has eased the problem of the tension between individual cadence in growing to adulthood and social acceptance of adulthood.

[33] *Trends,* p. 441.

[34] *Trends,* p. 680. The war caused a reversal here, which will probably hold for three or four years, since adolescents copy those a few years older. But the long-term trends will probably reassert themselves.

[35] *Trends,* pp. 414–415, 419.

problems involved in adjustment to the increased regimentation of industrial and commercial life. So that trends in mechanization[36] are important, and those in the building of "chain systems," large corporations, or other combinations that give relatively little chance for individual tempo.[37]

[36] J. S. Plant, "The Importance of New Developments in Machine Operations," *American Journal of Psychiatry,* vol. 93, no. 4, pp. 879–887, January 1937. There are very large areas of production that are still not on an assembly-line basis. However, the trend is in that direction, and much of the labor union movement implies a standardization of each day's work for everyone.

[37] *Trends,* pp. 238–249.

CHAPTER 7

Integration in the Sense of Self-sufficiency

We see children who have the problem of developing internal resources which result in a sort of wholeness of the personality. The clinical picture of success here is that of the older child or adult who feels at ease in or enjoys periods of being alone, without habitually using them as a refuge from ordinary social relationships. It is even quite possible that those who are most comfortable in their social relationships are precisely those who can the most genuinely "afford" to be alone.

In my own formulations I have tied together the capacity for this sort of mechanical detachment from the distractions of a busy world with the subsequently developing capacity for freeing oneself from various emotional entanglements. The latter issue can be most dramatically expressed in the teasing apart of the threads involved in love[1] and dependence.[2] For the first days and weeks of life the belongingness and dependence aspects of the parent-child relationship are closely interwoven—in fact, they seem mutually to arouse and strengthen each other. As the child grows and develops the kind of integration that is related to self-sufficiency, his dependency ties should weaken[3] though his love ties continue and perhaps even strengthen. This example is used only because it so clearly represents a problem to so many people. Parents often feel acutely that a child's growing self-sufficiency really endangers the strongest of family ties, and many of the older children who come to the clinic appear confused and depressed to a marked

[1] Chapter 1.   [2] Chapter 16.
[3] Plant, pp. 175–178.

degree because they associate less dependence with less belongingness.

   The larger problem of integration seems to present two distinct aspects—that which will be discussed in the next chapter in
relation to the sense of cohesion and that which is taken up in the
present chapter in relation to the sense of self-sufficiency. At-
tached to the latter aspect, in turn, are two types of problems.
The difficulties arising from the first type appear acutely quite
early in life.[4] They cluster around the need of each of us to develop enough internal resources but not too many—or too en-
grossing ones. What the proper balance is here, is a highly individual matter.[5] Probably no one ever quite satisfies himself that
he has found and maintained the perfect balance between living
and not *having* to live in the world about him.
   Our own data on the problem of self-sufficiency are probably
very one-sided. Working largely in a congested area, we have felt
that most of our children are conditioned by possessions and
schedules. Early in life they have too many toys, too many provided amusements and interests, too many invitations to watch
the workings of mechanical marvels. Thus we frequently find
children looking for escape in external things—always dependent
upon something they can *do* or *touch* or *see*. We have no data of
our own from rural areas, where we suspect much more self-sufficiency would be evident. This problem constantly interweaves
with that of extraversion,[6] and I have discussed it elsewhere.[7]

   The struggle to attain integration, or internal wholeness, begins somewhere around the age of six months and continues
through life, as the individual meets the challenge of the exter-

---

[4] For the second type, see pp. 96 f.
[5] See the discussion of emotional maturity, Chapters 16–19.
[6] Chapter 11.   [7] Plant, p. 289.

nal world. The list of trends affecting this area is very long. Among the most important are: the trends in the sale of toys;[8] those in various "things that are done for the child," such as music lessons;[9] those in the sale of automobiles and other mechanical contrivances[10] that demand minimum contributions in effort from the individual;[11] those in the development of national and cultural interests that seem to allow one to "escape from one-self";[12] those in economic shifts of material possessions.[13] Younger children give a clinical picture of being "softened" or "blasé" or "lacking in resourcefulness" because of the wealth of external answers to all the things they may want in life. When they grow older, there is a constant demand for continuance of the supply of these external satisfactions, as no internal resources have been built up. During the 1930's, however, we often saw a surprising reversal of this picture. Many children were forced by the financial depression to discover all sorts of internal resources for recreation—resources that had been hitherto completely blanketed under the amount of commercial recreation to which they had been exposed.

I have often wondered whether the present trend in our Western culture towards reliance on social "machinery" is a result, in part, of this same factor. Every problem—delinquency, school failure, marital unhappiness—is being met by building an agency or technique to control it. We are therefore interested in trends in the construction of laws and other agencies to control and improve various human relationships.[14]

By four or five years the child meets the threat to integration

[8] *Trends,* p. 952.   [9] *Trends,* pp. 788 ff.
[10] *Trends,* pp. 790, 940. A movie theatre on a Saturday afternoon hardly fits the adjective "passive." But even here the major part of the drama and action are provided *for* the child.
[11] *Trends,* p. 889.   [12] *Trends,* pp. 152–156, 187.
[13] *Trends,* pp. xxix–xxx (which is a condensation of Chapter v).
[14] *Trends,* p. 1288.

that comes from crowding.[15] In the reference just given I have outlined at some length our experience with the extent to which crowding in the home and neighborhood threatens the wholeness, the self-sufficiency, of the individual. The situation is of course affected by trends in urbanization[16] and urban housing[17] as well as by trends that involve crowding in schools, recreation, and industry.[18]

The clinical data are not clear here: (1) One sees irritable, tense, ill-at-easeness which develops into temper outbursts in the younger children of these crowded homes. It is as though their nerves were frayed by the constant effort of adjusting to others. A lumberman jumping from log to log—never able to take a moment's relaxation—would show the same picture if he were not allowed to rest. And these youngsters never are; even in their sleep others crowd close. As they grow older, various escape phenomena appear. They stay away from home as much as possible and keep late hours, but their restlessness seems more a residual habit of earlier nervous fatigue than a matter of the moment. (2) The symptom-complex of the city worker develops at an early age. It includes the factors that go into the organizer—the person who knows how the group works, how to get along with fellow men. These factors do not always predominate—that is, all persons who grow up in crowded homes are not successful organizers, or even members of organized groups, but a large fraction have a certain acceptance of the "way others will try to win their place." (3) Mingled with the other two is a picture we see developing around the age of ten, as some children adopt the attitude "Well, it doesn't make any difference how I behave." This, again, doesn't really flower until years later, when we see it in the anonymity of the large city. Such anonymity, we must remember, results less from the size of the city than from the individual's feeling that he

---

15 Plant, Chapter 8.   16 *Trends*, pp. 445–451.
17 *Trends*, pp. 471–476, 702.
18 E.g., mass attendance at spectacles (*Trends*, pp. 929–930).

doesn't count—that he has place and importance only as part of a crowd. Yet his identification is only with the crowd's activities, not with the crowd itself.

The wellsprings of the above picture are equally confused. Though the individual's sense of completeness often seems to be broken in upon by constant pressure from his group, the diffused pressure of a much larger group often has the opposite effect. At what point the pressure of the group becomes impersonal is beyond prediction. It even changes for the same individual from hour to hour as his preoccupations more or less shut out the external world. To some extent there are purely mechanical factors involved here; they do not create the whole picture, but a great part.

The reader will wonder why in this chapter the presence of others sometimes leads to incompleteness of the personality, whereas in Chapter 3 the same mechanical phenomenon leads to the building of an ever thicker wall of status preservation. I wish that I knew the answer. It has always seemed to me that the problem of this chapter arose from the presence, the movement, and the "show" of many people and many happenings; and that the problem of status preservation arose only where these other persons prodded or meddled into one's affairs. This may be the correct explanation, but I should be the first to admit the ease with which data may be used to support rather than adorn a theory.

At this point it would be interesting to know what village life does to the integration of the personality. We see relatively little of this in our clinic material, but what we have indicates that the "support" of the village, as it thrusts itself into all the joys and sorrows of the individual, tends to threaten his self-sufficiency. Occasionally we have seen youngsters from outlying areas of Essex County who were thought of as "one of the X family" and so were marked from their first appearance for better or for worse.

Though this semirural pattern does not give rise to the restless tenseness found in those who are always crowded next to others, it does tend to standardize behavior in such a way that there is a definite threat to "living one's own life." We are therefore interested in trends towards and away from the development of village life in America.[19] I have always assumed that in the definitely rural pattern there was every invitation to the development of self-sufficiency, but we have no data on this. It will be remembered that the large farm represents the one American pattern not seen in Essex County.

A special aspect of the problem of integration begins to appear when the child is about ten. He has passed through the phases of wanting to be a fireman or a grocer, and now starts to make a picture of his part in the total situation, of setting up goals and establishing values that will be more or less persistent. As time goes on, this picture will become more definite. The emphasis of the problem changes: so far people and material objects have seemed to threaten him physically; now they threaten the way he is going to live. The resulting reactions are not really different from those in the previous section, though they are less physical. Thus one might speak of restless or anxious or fidgety values— goals which aren't solid or comfortably standing by the child because the clamor of conflicting interests keeps them from maturing in their own right. Or one might speak of values completely untouched by the influences of others because there are *so many* others that none has any real claim on the individual.

In other words, without any real change in the mechanisms involved we can see the problem "elevated" from the purely physical field to that of the child's goals or values.

One more question in this area demands a hearing. Is the ex-

19 *Trends*, pp. 509–520.

tent of crowding in this country related to our penchant for joining organizations? Theoretically this should be so. There is a very
considerable body of data on the trends in size and number of social and fraternal organizations,[20] but this has not been broken
down into the matter of answering three preliminary questions.
Do these organizations flourish in cities rather than in rural areas?
Is there disproportionate recruiting from the more crowded sections of the city? Do members come disproportionately from large
and crowded families? This is of course not to say that there is
only one reason for organizations—or for joining them.

The second type of problem related to the attainment of self-
sufficiency is concerned with the individual's essential willingness or ability to accept the consequences of errors and failures.
From the first it is complicated by the unwillingness or inability
of the parents to wean the child emotionally.[21] There are at least
six factors that work for or against this. The first two and the
fourth weigh heavily against the child's chance of developing his
own personality, free from adult pressures. The third weighs in
his favor. The last two, in their emphasis on the psychological
problems involved in family relationships, tend to emphasize his
need for freedom towards his own growth. (1) Many parents simply do not realize that it is not enough to wean their children;
they must also wean themselves from their children. (2) Many
parents who have suffered devastating disappointments frankly
accept the need to correct their errors or failures in the lives of
their children. In all love they must watch and control every
movement. (3) To a certain extent these parental needs and pressures are released by trends in the development of extrafamily activities, such as wage earning for the mother, cultural interests,
recreation, and the like.[22] (4) Theoretically, at least, financial de-

---

[20] *Trends,* p. 935.   [21] See Chapter 16, pp. 200 f.
[22] *Trends,* Chapter XIV.

pressions involving unemployment and a smaller flow of money place a heavier load on family relationships and so increase family tension.[23] (5) As the mechanics of living come more and more to be taken for granted, there is increased preoccupation with the relationships of living.[24] (6) Finally, the advantages of emotional maturity are constantly stressed in the public print and in the field of general education.

Whether or not we wish to follow a large school in believing that the trauma of being born conditions the individual's reaction to every new experience through the rest of life, the possibility remains that it seriously impedes the weaning process through the early months of life. There is no statistically established relationship between the difficulty of the process of birth and the amount of trauma which the child's fear of the new connotes, but if we are prepared to accept Rank's work,[25] then it is fair to assume that difficult birth experiences tend to produce a deeper fear of whatever is new or venturesome.

In any case, it must be remembered that for some months the child does not wish to be weaned and that the process is affected by the supernumeraries in the family. Each one is an extra hazard against the child's chance to grow up as himself—free from the need of adults to make their lives whole through him. We are therefore interested in the various trends involving the disappearance of the large family and the extended or clan family.[26] In the latter case the question is not so much whether various relatives live in the same house with the child as the much subtler question whether the spirit of the clan is kept alive by relatives

---

[23] But life so often defies our theory. During the last depression we *should* have had a sharp increase in school tardiness, school absence, truancy, and delinquency (good yardsticks of family tension). Just the opposite occurred!

[24] *Trends,* pp. 666–672.

[25] E.g., Otto Rank, *The Trauma of Birth* (New York, Harcourt, 1929).

[26] Mildred Parten, "A Statistical Analysis of the Modern Family," *Annals of the American Academy of Political and Social Science,* vol. 160, pp. 32, 35 ff., March 1932.

living in the neighborhood or at much greater traveling distance. And even this last is complicated by the fact that while fewer aunts, uncles, and grandparents decrease the number of adults developing the child's dependence—precisely the same thing intensifies the parent-child relationship.[27] The opposed strengths of these two influences show every conceivable variation.

Handicaps such as lameness, poor vision, physical weakness, low intelligence, and emotional instability also delay the weaning process in that they make the individual feel that it is dangerous to stand alone. Though occasionally we see an exceptional case in which a defect seems to "throw the child back on himself" and thus to foster integration, handicapped children in general tend to show increased or prolonged dependence. Therefore we are interested in trends as to the number and treatment of crippling conditions in children[28] and, equally, in trends in recognizing the mental symptoms involved in such conditions.[29]

In addition to these personal factors, there is the whole group of difficulties arising from the demands of the environment. The problems that are involved here and the various possible ways in which the child responds to these pressures have been covered in Chapter 6.

A new factor enters when the child begins to feel that his own mistakes can be corrected through the lives of his children. This usually happens around the age of twelve. Sometimes a youngster will say, "Believe me, doctor, no child of mine will ever go through *this*." Here is the beginning of dependence upon one's

[27] One of the most dramatic developments of our generation is this concentration of the emotional load upon individuals in the melting away of the clan family. Each of us "has to mean so much more to another."

[28] White House Conference (Section IV, Committee B), *The Handicapped Child* (New York, Century, 1933), pp. 4–9.

[29] E. A. Doll, *Mental Deficiency Due to Birth Injuries* (New York, Macmillan, 1932).

children as there was earlier dependence upon one's parents. Essentially an adult problem, we mention it here only by way of indicating the time when we see it emerge. Rooted in the individual and growing out of his needs long before his children begin to arrive, it seems to play a part in the choice of future occupations that will give advisory control over others. We are therefore interested in trends in the belief in afterlife or other such mechanisms which free one from the burden of "squaring his accounts" in his own life or the lives of his children.[30]

It is only fair to state here once more an important warning which I have often given. Physicians always have skewed data. Those individuals who do not need to twist and mold their children in order to patch warped lives are probably in families that we think would be less likely to come to the psychiatrist. The physician says that people who eat pickles get stomachaches—because they are the ones who come to him. After constant pressure from that sort of thing, it becomes easy for him to make a general rule—forgetting that he hasn't the slightest bit of real evidence whether there are a million people who eat pickles without getting stomachaches.

At the outset two groups of problems were mentioned as relating to self-sufficiency. One of these has been traced into mid-adolescence, where our material stops. The origin of the other has also been traced, though it bulks largely at a date not covered by our material. The latter problem is roughly that of being willing to pay the fiddler—to dance without asking someone else to foot the bill. It is simple of statement but extremely stubborn against solution. The psychiatrist begins to hear of it when the child is somewhere around twelve. Of course children begin at a much earlier age to dream of being rid of many of their present problems when they grow up, but it is not until adolescence that they

[30] *Trends*, p. 411.

definitely plan to repair their own mischances in the lives of their children. The whole matter is the result of a subtle sort of rationalization. The drive to have children is well-nigh undeniable, and each of us is the product of a highly selective heredity, which down through the ages has been intensifying this urge. It is comforting to believe that we are going to see the growing generation develop a better world—one devoid of our own mistakes. But the critical question as to any specific plan for the child is whether it is really for the child's advancement or the parent's compensation.[81]

These two groups of problems seem to me to be different aspects of a more fundamental problem. It would be nice to be sure that better integration in the first group presages more self-sufficiency in the second. I have no data on this point. Perhaps a relationship does not exist.

[81] If I say that this is entirely unfair to the child, it is not with the slightest idea that anything will be changed in the near future. In a sense, the younger generation always has to pay for the mistakes of the elder. This fact is overlooked by citizens who get into a frenzy over governmental spending for which their children will have to pay.

CHAPTER 8

Integration in the Sense of Cohesion

We see children who have the problem of adjustment to being "different people at different times." In part this is a problem of the child's accepting and being tolerant of the different individuals he seems to be. In part, also, it is the problem of selecting one of his "personalities" and setting it up as a sort of moderator of the others, since considerations of both efficiency and comfort demand a workable federation of these loosely-held-together units.

Inner division does not seem in itself an abnormal circumstance. Most of us feel that we are made up of many parts. We use different language, fall easily into radically different situations, and even feel physically different in different situations. Each part seems to possess real integrity—to be whole at the time of its ascendancy—to lay claims against other equally complete integers of the total personality. The explanation may be that a certain core of attitudes, abilities, and physical reactions runs through all these different people that each of us feels he is.

But the problem isn't easy for those who have too much or too little coordination. People to whom we perhaps naïvely attribute a "peasant" mind seem to have only one personality. Children of this type aren't able to describe themselves as undergoing certain experiences; they have to relive those experiences. If they argue out a point of conduct, they have to externalize one of the points of view. On the other hand children who have "too many personalities," each with too much integrity and importance to bow before the rest, are quite as vulnerable in the face of problems as those who cannot objectify themselves at all. The very multiplicity of claims—and their balance—make incisive action and dynamic goals and values impossible. It seems as if too close and efficient a federation leads to bigoted intolerance as to one's life, whereas looseness of federation makes for indecision and a frittering away of capacities.

The number of these so-called personalities is determined by inheritance or by something that happens so early in life that from a clinical point of view it may be considered as congenital. There also seems to be some correlation between the number of personalities and whatever it is that the psychologist calls intelligence (which is certainly congenitally determined). In any case, as I have noted elsewhere,[1] I have had great difficulty in effecting any change in an individual's capacity to develop a different number of subpersonalities. As to trends, the important matter is the prevalence of one or another type in any cultural pattern and the change (if any) that occurs as individuals move from one pattern to another.[2]

In some respects the development of the individual's subpersonalities is similar to that of his member rôles, which also begin to form early in life.[3] The processes are concurrent, and it is not clear to the child himself that one is primarily individual in origin and the other primarily sociological. As I understand it, the sociologist does not know how member rôles form or how they

[1] Plant, pp. 76–77.

[2] This point runs all through a book by R. E. L. Faris and H. W. Dunham, *Mental Disorders in Urban Areas* (University of Chicago Press, 1939). The data is oriented to the problem of mental breakdown.

The Mental Hygiene Study of the Eastern Health District of Baltimore, Maryland, has been approaching this problem for years, again from the point of view of mental breakdown. It is the most carefully done and extensive study of its sort, and there have been numerous reports and papers. For reference to these and a general discussion, see Christopher Tietze, Paul Lemkau, and Marcia Cooper, "Personality Disorder and Spatial Mobility," *American Journal of Sociology*, vol. 48, no. 1, pp. 29–39, July 1942.

[3] See footnote 16, p. 13.

get themselves over to the individual. He uses the convenient formula "formal and informal pressures," which doesn't tell us very much, though the psychiatrist has no better way of saying it. Certainly, a girl somehow gets to know what is expected of girls—and fathers, farmers, teachers, Catholics, Americans, each in some intuitive way knows what this means. I say "intuitively" because often the most insistent parts of member rôles are things which we cannot trace in our experience. For some time I thought that identification was important here—being a father is being "like my father" or "like John's father." This may be the case, though in actual clinical practice one is often told, "Though I am a teacher, I've never known a single person who is what I really think a teacher should be." Whatever the source, these member rôles draw and quarter our loyalties and attitudes. Even our dressing for the day is subject to conflicts.[4]

It must, then, be evident that the problem of integration is somewhat the same for the various "personalities" of the individual as for his member rôles, for in each instance there must emerge a feeling of "I" in the face of disparate entities. It differs, however, in at least two important respects: (1) As the various personalities develop, overlapping is reduced or disappears. The individual finds that he can live comfortably in a number of different environments or "sets," if he can keep them from interfering with each other. Quite the opposite is the case with member rôles. For example, a prisoner has one member rôle with his fellow prisoners, and another with the warden. Even the languages of these two member rôles are opposed—"obedience" is a bad term in one, a good term in the other. Easement comes to the extent that this overlapping can be increased—to the extent that the common denominator can be enlarged. (2) The development of the

---

[4] As pointed out later in the chapter, one of the sources of the efficiency of a totalitarian set-up is that (for the individual) it erases the problem of warring member rôles ("I am primarily a Nazi; whatever conflicts with that member rôle simply doesn't exist").

different personalities is obviously dependent, to a certain degree, on the cultural components of the environment, but the individual feels that he is master of the situation—that as he fits into this or that situation, it is of his own choosing. Member rôles, on the other hand, are externally decided—what I am as a father is, in some dim way, determined by all the fathers who have ever lived. Here I am but a minute part of a great pageant which presses in upon me. Once more I remember that I don't know just how these pressures are gotten over to me, but here they are, in not-to-be-denied insistence.

According to the psychoanalytic group, by the age of three,[5] the child is able to recognize a security-giving parent and an authority-wielding parent and is beginning to identify himself with these different pictures. I have observed this phenomenon but have no evidence that the child develops different personalities in the process.[6] It is true, however, that by this time the child is developing his superego,[7] so that objectivity is operative within the personality—one part watching the other. There may be here the beginning of the development of these subpersonalities—only I haven't seen it as such in my material.

At about four the child becomes definitely aware of the imposition of different personalities upon him through remarks of his parents—"This is my good boy, my bad boy has gone away." And soon he begins using similar expressions—"It was the bad boy who did that." Just how seriously this represents the youngster's thinking of himself as two or more persons, it is hard to say because of the very strong adult appeal that such formulae have. One has to admit that all the way up to the stage of adult crime there is the frequent "I don't know why I did it—it must have been another

[5] See p. 60.   [6] Plant, pp. 128–138.
[7] How much this is part of the growth process and how much it is determined by the immediate environment of the child, are matters of conjecture.

me." How often this is a reality and how often a heart-softening excuse is one of our difficult and unsolved questions.

By the age of six, however, many children and perhaps all begin to feel that they don't understand some of the things they do. This is a different matter from that discussed in the previous section, though perhaps a development of it. Here we are dealing with matters which the child seems to fight against, which urge themselves upon him against his will. While this appears in all sorts of deeds and misdeeds, it is particularly dramatic in the so-called conflict cases described by Healy[8] and occasionally seen by everyone.[9] I think it worth noting that in our clinic experience the child does not feel that this drive comes from another personality—rather he says "Some other part of me that I don't understand makes me do it." This may, however, be the start of his feeling that he is really a number of different people.

Certainly by eight a great many children behave in an entirely different way when they are away from home. Conversely, many others have the very simple but thoroughly disquieting difficulty of being unable to split themselves naturally in this way. Thus when they explode some "dirty words" in Sunday school, often it is not that they are more sex conscious than others but that they haven't built efficient walls to separate their various selves. By eight, what we are pleased to call the "normal" child knows pretty well that there is a place for everything; the "problem" child is merely one who puts everything into the same place.

It is hard to date the next stage of this problem—perhaps ten is as near as any to the age at which the child begins "naturally"

[8] All through his writings but perhaps best in *Reconstructing Behavior in Youth* (New York, Knopf, 1929).

[9] The popular conception of the kleptomaniac is the simplest illustration that comes to mind.

to associate his different personalities with different situations. Up to this time he has been using different language in various situations, but apparently there has been an element of effort in it; he has had to suppress the words and attitudes of one situation while in another. At ten, however, we begin to see this company of separate personalities forming as such. It would be interesting to know whether, somewhat earlier, the child reacted differently (or was a "different person") with his sister than with his brother and just when this began. But this sort of data—which is not easy to obtain—is of questionable value, because so many of the play activities of young children are imposed upon them by adults, along with liberal doses of "how to behave" in certain situations or towards certain people.

Something undoubtedly happens to the envelope when the child is about ten. Up until that time it has been peculiarly permeable—the child seeming almost avidly to soak up any possible scraps of information on how one should act in any given situation. As above noted[10] a selective process has been operating for some two or three years in the matter of expression—what the child actually *does* in any situation. But from ten on he is much more aware of what he should see or hear in certain places or from certain people, and the envelope acts to shut out improper material or to explain it away or to translate it—in short to give personality what it can afford to accept.

The trends here seem very important. Among other things, they include the number of different experiences that are offered to the child[11] and the extent to which such experiences are specialized.[12] The problem is intensified and sharpened by certain

10 See p. 105.

11 Trends in the roaming range of children and in the heterogeneity of neighborhoods (*Trends*, pp. 173–178, 470–474).

12 Education, moral training, and recreation are being increasingly taken over by agencies with highly formalized patterns, which tend more and more to federalize themselves and to be less and less responsive to the neighborhood or family demands (*Trends*, pp. 363, 1281, 1282, 1496–1504).

environmental factors that have developed largely in the last two generations. Of chief importance are: the radio, bringing incompatible situations into close juxtaposition;[13] the telephone—less dramatic than the radio, but more personal; and the automobile.[14] It would seem that when the things that impinge upon the child's life are directed towards a luxuriant development of only one part of his total personality, we present every inducement towards the splitting apart of various subpersonalities.

It may be that phantasy plays some part in this problem. Certainly many children are able to construct vivid and compelling pictures of themselves as different persons in different situations. This must make it easier to develop or accept a federation of personalities. The situation does not seem quite the same as that in which normal adults, while indulging in a great deal of phantasy, apparently realize that the imaginary self does not constitute an efficient separate personality. However, I have never seen a youngster in whom it appeared that the dream life played any such rôle as phantasies seem to. That is, I have never seen a child whose dreams were so vivid or meaningful, that he would not say, "Oh, that was only a dream."

So far we have considered only those aspects of the problem which involve the multiplication of subpersonalities. By twelve the problem begins to be complicated by the development of a goal—of what will some day be a central core of meaning around which the individual attempts to cluster his various rôles or personalities. As will appear in the next section, this involves values —of which I see little indication at this early age. Now the emphasis is on vocational choice. Whether this provides a basis for later development, I don't know. It must be evident that there are vigorous trends[15] which make it difficult for the child to free

---

[13] Plant, pp. 137–138.   [14] *Trends*, p. 177.   [15] *Trends*, p. 358.

himself from the mesh of feeling that the problem of goals is really only a problem of vocational choice. Almost each year sees a new multiplication of vocational aptitude tests. Moreover, there is still a widespread belief that the matter of vocational choice is an equipment problem rather than a drive problem. A great deal of vocational counseling is still on the basis of advising a person to go into what he can do best rather than of assaying the chances he has of succeeding in what he wants to do. It is amazing how frequently a clinic such as ours is bombarded with requests for tests to tell the child "what he should be as an adult."

From this standpoint we see very little delinquency, though there is much confusion in children, evidenced by such things as: (1) lack of interest in school work—where no vocational choice is developed, or the one developed doesn't seem to fit into the child's school curriculum; (2) a negative sort of floating, which parents usually term "moping"; (3) an inefficiency described as "laziness"—which is made more acute by the testing programs of our better school systems;[16] (4) a truculent sort of complaining that "life has nothing worth while to offer."

By sixteen the values which the child has been building up begin to crystallize around a total philosophy of life. In such patterns as ours, there is a tendency to drive the child to some point of success without offering any core for the integration of his personality.[17] There are important trends here, including the very rapid increase in the access that conflicting claims have to the child through advertising.[18] One should, I suppose, write an entire chapter on the failure of American education to teach the im-

---

[16] Very often the schools refer these youngsters, not because they are doing badly, but because they are failing to get the marks indicated by their I.Q.'s. There would probably be a certain amount of humor in the situation for the adolescents themselves if there were not so much tension.

[17] *Trends*, p. 358. So far as this is a part of the whole process of democratization, see J. S. Plant, "Objectives for Children in a Democratic Society," *Annals of the American Academy of Political and Social Science*, vol. 212, pp. 223–230, particularly p. 227, November 1940.

[18] *Trends*, p. 910.

portance of values, and on the personal confusion that has attended the assumption by the individual of this function of setting his own values as a part of the process of democratization.

One segment of the problem demands mention because it brings so many children to a guidance group. The reader will recognize it as a link between the matters of the previous section and the present one. This has to do with courtship customs—children, particularly girls, becoming confused over what "home training" has dictated in boy-and-girl activities and "what they hear now" as to the road to success in becoming popular.

As we come to the close of the age period with which I work, the whole problem of integration begins to take on sharper outlines because of certain peculiarities in our cultural pattern. (1) Life becomes sufficiently analyzed to allow, or even demand, entirely different ethical standards in various of its parts. The classroom is often so crowded and so impersonal that children have no difficulty in developing the attitude of "getting away with anything you can" at school when they have no such attitude at home. The trends that are important are those in the geographical separation of recreational, educational, and family aspects of the child's life;[19] and also those in the crystallization of codes of ethics for various aspects of life—a "business code" allowing much more ruthless competition than a "good neighbor code" or "family code." (2) This breakdown[20] goes so far that even in the vocation of one's choice there is sometimes a demand that the individual show deep interest in what is ordinarily repugnant to him. For example, the successful lawyer must be interested in defending clients regardless of their guilt or of the moral issues involved; the successful doctor must be interested in surgery. Some bright day psychiatrists may find that all surgeons are really sa-

[19] *Trends*, p. 451. This is a résumé of several preceding pages touching the subject.
[20] *Trends*, pp. 296–297.

distic at heart, but until then we shall go on believing that the interests and benefits of the profession "shut out" a feeling of repugnance to the cold cutting up of other people. (3) There is the question (so far unanswered) as to what mechanized factory work does to the problem of personality integration. On the one hand, automatic industrial processes require little training or special ability, so that the personality has little to focus on.[21] On the other hand, it has been suggested[22] that when automatic industrial processes are pushed into the unconscious, the personality may be freed to integrate on a higher level. The trends to be watched here are those in the automatization of industrial and commercial occupations;[23] those in the substitution of techniques and standards for individual judgment in professional work; and those in the employment of maintenance rather than production workers.[24]

Some mention must be made of schizophrenia even though it rarely occurs in full-blown form before the age of sixteen. This comprises a group of difficulties in which at least one of the outstanding symptoms is that of the breaking up of the federation of personalities. Consequently, we should expect that the social trends mentioned in the previous section would result in a sharp increase in the incidence of the disease. The interesting fact is that while a slow increase actually occurs,[25] this is proportionately small; apparently some mechanism (which we do not yet understand) acts as a compensator for the analyzing factors of the en-

---

21 *Trends*, p. 853, summarizes this.
22 E.g., Elton Mayo, *Human Problems of an Industrial Civilization* (New York, Macmillan, 1933).
23 *Trends*, p. 806.
24 J. S. Plant, "The Importance of New Developments in Machine Operations," *American Journal of Psychiatry*, vol. 93, no. 4, pp. 879–887, January 1937.
25 Carney Landis and J. D. Page, *Modern Society and Mental Disease* (New York, Farrar, 1938), Chapter XII.

vironment. Undoubtedly here, as elsewhere, the envelope also plays a rôle in protecting the personality from a full realization of the extent to which the analytical environment invites a similar fractionation.

CHAPTER 9

Physical Expression of the Sexual Urge

We see children who have the problem of adjusting themselves to the various phases of the maturation of the sexual urge in its physical sense, to the fact of the relatively intense response arising from sexual stimulation, and to the fact that "raw," unsublimated expressions of sexual hunger are not acceptable to the society in which they live. There are few, if any, persons who strike a comfortable balance between satisfaction of sexual hunger and satisfaction of a society which with equal inexorability demands that this urge shall always be turned into socially useful channels. These pressures are so compelling and at such variance with each other that one can only do his best in serving two masters.

The separation of this problem from that of the following chapter (use of sexual expressions for their language values) has long seemed to me to be necessary. Owing to the potency and importance of the sex drive, society has long since endowed it with meaning almost equal to that placed upon the considerations of self-preservation. These symbolic, or language, values attain enormous significance for the individual—usually becoming even more important to him than physical satisfaction.

Even during infancy the genital area is richly supplied with sensory nerves, so that from the start excitation in these zones produces more results than similar stimulation elsewhere. At the beginning the feelings aroused in the child are not sexual in our adult sense of the word. Indeed the very first reactions appear to be disturbing rather than either pleasant or unpleasant in connotation. Soon they are more pleasant than unpleasant, though with slight intensification unpleasant components emerge. (In the next chapter we shall encounter many instances of the carrying through of sexual activities, even when they are unpleasant, for the sake of their language value.)

As the child grows, the reverberations of sexual excitation (which earlier seemed to go through the whole body) become more and more localized in the genital region and are more clearly recognized as arising in that area. Through all this appears the central problem of the present chapter—that of weighing the invitation to pleasant experiences against the taboo our culture places upon such activity. However, there is always the complication of the language factors[1]—a large part of sexual expression being merely a means to attain other ends. Some proof of this lies in the relative ease with which sexual interests are dropped when there are other simple and easy ways of attaining recognition, position, and what not. Since children who are mentally or physically handicapped would naturally have more than the usual difficulty in finding other outlets, we should expect to find them often presenting stubborn problems of undue sexual interest. Only now we see that these are really problems of inadequate outlet through more socially acceptable channels.[2]

Even in very early childhood the fact that the genitalia offer such a ready approach to the visceral nervous system makes them the source of unusual return in response to stimuli.[3] When masturbation is practiced by young children great perturbation evidently takes place through the whole body, as the face flushes and the pulse and breathing are stepped up—but we see it only

[1] Chapter 10.
[2] Plant, in many places, but particularly pp. 220 f.
[3] Rabid devotees of psychogenetic theories could well attune their motif to the fact that nowhere else in the body can manipulation of any sort so efficiently produce reverberations through the system that controls the feelings. The anus and mouth present somewhat less practicable sources of the same thing. Has this anything to do with the usual development away from oral- and anal-eroticism?

rarely. This is almost always a behavior problem, belonging in Chapter 10 rather than here.

This richness of sensory mechanisms plays a large rôle in the sex play of children ("playing doctor," etc.). However, one must not forget that a poor sexual adjustment between the parents unquestionably plays a very large rôle here. Such adults tend to read a great deal of sexual meaning into acts which are practically neutral at the start. They sternly place a taboo, and from then on the child gets as much or more satisfaction because the acts are noticed than because they are sexual. By the time such situations come to the psychiatrist, the authority, guilt, and recognition problems have usually completely masked the original problem of physical satisfaction. In this connection I have often wondered about the rapid growth of literature dealing with sexual problems in children or, rather, with what are claimed to be sexual problems in children. I suppose it would be difficult to determine how much the spread of this literature is the result of sexual maladjustment and how much the result of the prestige that comes from turning a neutral act into a difficulty.

From six to eleven there is an intensification of the earlier problems, and it is much easier to confuse the issues with those of the language values. In fact, the latter grow with leaps and bounds as the child begins to recognize the intense preoccupation of his culture in the problem of sex and the intricate camouflage that it has constructed in consequence. For instance, while it is true that masturbation now admits of far more intense emotional returns, these have a large fraction of pain in them and the child is more interested in "finding out how it works" or of "doing what older people do" than in direct physical satisfaction. Curiosity and the need to identify with the strong and big are the dominant elements.

While we occasionally see children who have developed real

satisfaction during this six-to-eleven period from perversions such as sodomy, the majority are either forced into the situation or participate for money or to "stand in" with older children. Even the few who take the active rôle in the perversion seem to derive more satisfaction from dominance of the social group than from the physical act.

I have felt that the statements in the previous paragraph—which are based simply on what children say—are somewhat reinforced by the fact that practically none of the children of this age referred by school or court come from areas where there is adequate emotional outlet. Obviously any child can be forced into playing the passive rôle in one or another sex perversion, but in the case of those actively so engaged or those coming to us for interest in dirty notes or pictures or in salacious magazines, or for using foul language, we have never yet found that we were dealing with youngsters who were getting real satisfaction out of educational or social activities. This may be due to one or another of many reasons. I have felt that the simplest explanation is that where sufficient status is achieved from socially accepted modes of competition, there is no need to develop it through the sexual channels. These last are so dramatic for children that if the sexual urge were as great a part of the dynamics of life as the psychoanalytic group would have us believe, we should see this mode of expression turned to far more often, and we should have more evidence of direct sexual satisfaction arising from it. Through this whole area the trends in broadening the base of criteria upon which the child is graded in school are obviously of the greatest interest and importance.[4]

Towards the end of this six-to-eleven period the various abnormalities of the sex organs begin to be noticed (though prob-

---

[4] Prescott, p. 247.

ably here also the language values are the more important consideration). Thus peculiarly large or small primary or secondary
sex characters are the source of a great deal of anxiety and of fur-
tive comparison, and even when no abnormalities exist the
youngster may wonder "whether there aren't going to be" or see
them in variations that are well within the normal range. There
are, at present, no accepted standards for the development of the
secondary sex characters. The trends (e.g., with the child-develop-
ment groups) towards setting up norms of physiological and
anatomical growth are going to be of the greatest importance
here. They will give us fairly certain limits within which we
shall know we are dealing with normal variation, but will markedly increase the anxiety states of parents and early adolescents.
In the case of children who are anxious over small or poorly developed secondary sex characters, I have no reliable data as to
how much of this is primary and how much is caught by contagion
from the parents. In the latter instance, we have an illustration of
a definite disturbance sweeping into the personality with little
hindrance or change in the envelope—as this, obviously, has had
little or no intimation from the personality of a need for protection.

However, the frequency with which we have found children
peculiarly lacking in disturbance over marked retardation in
sexual maturation is perhaps the clearest indication of the fact
that sexual development is really psychosexual development.
This lack of disturbance may be an integral part of the retardation, and if so, then there should be, in later years, a crushing feeling over this same failure.

Glandular imbalance (e.g., of the anterior pituitary) begins
towards the end of this period to point up more definite and dramatic crises. It is true that symptoms show in the earlier years
but don't impress the child as being unusual. Children under
eight rarely show anxiety over physical abnormalities produced
by glandular dysfunction though parents frequently are much

disturbed and others who are dealing with the child's well-being often find clearly defined symptoms in these early years.

Perhaps the imbalance which is most distressing at this period is that which develops in the gonadal area with marked characteristics of the opposite sex. This presents an extremely complicated problem to the envelope, because in our own culture a high value is given to a certain admixture of the characteristics. We admire a certain softness in the boy and increasingly prize physical strength and rough-and-readiness in the girl. In each instance we say to the child that there must not be too much admixture from the opposite sex but give him very little help as to what we mean by this. (What the war will mean here, it is hard to guess. While putting a premium on masculinity in boys, it seems also to have asked for more masculinity in girls. However, one would guess that the swing towards defense work or entry into women's branches of the service might not last and that a stress upon femininity in girls would eventually be the outcome of the changed demands for boys.) These are the more normal or expected problems of this area. Of the unusual ones, it is our experience that the boy who is recognized as a sissy has a far more difficult problem to face than the girl who is rather masculine (this is apparently just the opposite of the balance reached after the first World War). Yet here once more we feel certain that in these early years the child is not so disturbed over the condition itself as over the fact that it connotes a *difference*. For instance, we have never run into a boy who felt tension, discomfort, or strangeness because of femininity, but we see all sorts of severe problems of inferiority arising because society teases such boys.

As adolescence approaches, the whole problem dramatically changes, since there develops a sharply marked pleasure factor in sexual expression.[5] It is difficult for parents, teachers, social work-

[5] But where the experiences are very rich, the pain component also enters. The mechanisms involved in this are perhaps best expressed in the work of G. Dumas,

ers, and other persons in authority to adjust to this change. The
child has been so nicely controlled in the earlier years by diver-
sion to other channels of expression and recognition that, with
the advent of adolescent changes, there is a bustling, hurried increase in the use of these same methods. In large part they work,
but once the child has discovered through physical experience
that here is an emotional return which cannot be equaled in any
other way, he is not to be denied in the furtherance of his sexual
quest. This is not meant to belittle the various efforts, through
academic or athletic or social success, towards replacing masturbation or heterosexual experiences of a usual or unusual sort.
Various socially acceptable outlets unquestionably manage to
prevent a great many adolescents from turning to the unsublimated sexual drive for satisfaction. Also, the matter of values may
frequently be a determining factor, depending upon the extent
to which the child has already adopted or built any very clear
goals or values and what he feels that he is willing to pay, in these
terms, for immediate satisfactions.[6] The fact remains that during
adolescence we have no immediate experience to offer the child
that equals the clear-cut pleasure involved in the completed sexual act (using this expression for the attainment of orgasm in
either homosexual or heterosexual experiences).

This is of great importance in understanding the so-called perversions of adolescence. For example, much of the sodomy
brought out in juvenile court has been accompanied by rich heterosexual phantasy, and the participants will undoubtedly seek
normal outlets as soon as the social situation allows. I differentiate between this sort of sodomy (which is only a makeshift im-

Nouveau Traité de psychologie (Paris, Felix Alcan, 1932), which is clearly summarized in Prescott, pp. 18 ff.

[6] All through here runs one more thread. Society has placed such a forbidding
taboo on sexual intercourse that once the child has gone "that far," he or she is apt
to run rather wildly through the whole field of physical sex relationships, as there
is little inducement to make further efforts at sublimation. As this is dependent
entirely on the cultural taboo, it is natural that we see the phenomenon much more
often in girls than in boys.

posed by the cultural taboo on heterosexual expression) and that
which is part of a true perversion in which the person never develops a heterosexual interest.[7] Thus the phantasy (e.g., "I pre-
tend that I'm doing it to a girl") accompanying the act is the critical matter.

What fraction of any sexual act represents direct physical urge
and what represents language value in the sense used in the following chapter, it is extremely difficult to decide. There are probably great individual differences—and in many cases equally varied fractionation for the same person at different times, though
whether these are due to inherited differences in the sexual appetite or to cultural conditioning, I don't know. In my clinical material both factors almost always enter. It is easier to find examples of pure language value, where the sexual act is actually painful to both parties, but gone through with because "it shows
that we are grown up" or "it shows that we are in love," than examples of unadulterated physical urge.

Somewhere around twelve there emerges an aspect of the problem of sexual development which defies satisfactory formulation,
though it is of great practical import. Without seriously pressing
the claims of accuracy in the field of the physical development of
the reflexes, it is possible to point out that those involved in
sphincter control, in speech, and in the sexual area have a certain
regularity in their relationships. I have named them roughly in
order of assured maturation, of finely balanced complexity, and
of importance to self-preservation. The more adventuresome
could extend the picture to include those reflexes of circulation
and alimentation that become established before birth. And

7 Admittedly this is on the basis of my own theory (Plant, particularly pp. 219–
223), which has been given scant place by other authors. The usual formulation is
to place the material in this chapter on the same level as Pareto's residues (see Appendix) and the material in Chapter 10 on the level of the derivatives of such residues. Though the two aspects of the sexual urge may be fused in later discussions,
it seems to me more practical to separate them at the present writing.

there is a further orderliness—that as we move through the heart, the intestines, the sphincters, speech, and sexual expression we meet mechanisms that are progressively unstable in adult life under the pressure of emotional tensions. Little children wet the bed under *any* serious stress (it was Mrs. Strachey, I believe, who pointed out that during the blitz of 1940 "half the mattresses in England" were "a-wash"). Older children present speech disorders (even in our common parlance one "stammers his thanks" or is "struck dumb with amazement") and find the sphincter reflexes much better stabilized. Even older persons show a marked improvement in the stability of speech (of all children with speech disorders something like five per cent have them as adults) and their tensions are, once more, registered in the most recently established reflex mechanisms—those of the sexual adjustments. Thus as a nation went to war, we saw a sharp increase in the marriage rate, in the birth rate, and in sex delinquency—as the most sensitive indicators of emotional stress. In some jurisdictions sex delinquency rose three hundred per cent over the pre-war figures. Though all sorts of matters contributed to this, it can be basically explained by the reflex mechanisms that emerge as the individual is subjected to heightened emotional tension. So, in what we might term an almost mechanical way, the twelve-year-older begins to find that tension and frustration are expressed as problems of sexual urge.

The sexual drive clearly becomes a problem in its own right between the ages of twelve and sixteen. Large areas of language value remain, but we no longer have to wonder what the child is trying to do or show or win or buy with this or that bit of sexual behavior. This has led to an enormous amount of confusion in the present generation. Until fairly recently the raw, unsublimated sexual drive was loaded with heavy sociological meaning. General ignorance of contraceptives meant a very high hazard that sexual intercourse would lead to pregnancy. The relative economic dependence of women and the great load of functions carried by the family meant that pregnancy involved a situation which very nearly encompassed the lives of the two involved.[8] Changes in these areas have done an interesting thing to the act of sexual intercourse—which can now be measured much more in terms of its immediate returns to those involved. We shall see in the next chapter what a complicated problem this has posed to the envelope, as new language values are built up around the sexual act. In the meantime we think we see not only an increase in sexual intercourse during this age period but an increase in the acceptance of the direct physical returns as a measure of its value. At least there is a great deal of this, though obviously we lack reliable comparative data from earlier generations.

During this period it cannot be denied that transitory sources of emotional satisfaction fail to equal that attained through the various erotic experiences. This offers a serious challenge to the whole program of sex education, where despite the full spread of physiological and anatomical information parents find it difficult to explain to children why sexual experiences should be delayed. During adolescence there are all sorts of "deferred returns" to which children wholeheartedly give their loyalty, and it is possible to set up these long-term goals as worthy compensations for the loss of the exquisite immediate pleasure. However, we have seen many children swept off their feet by torrents of emotion for which even very meticulous education as to sexual matters had given them absolutely no preparation.

A problem of especially stubborn insistence is that of "the second-rater." This youngster, less favored in intelligence or appearance or strength, now finds that he or she is as good as anyone else in open competition. The girl often finds herself sought after for the first time; and the boy, regardless of earlier failures

8 The trends in these two basic matters are given in *Trends*, pp. 151, 664–679.

of any sort, finds that the sexual orgasm (in loneliness or with another) brings as intense satisfaction to him as to anyone else. The problem of turning these second-raters away from sexual interests (once really started) thus becomes an extremely difficult one. Combined with that of ignorance as to contraception and disease, it forces us to the poignant necessity of providing younger children with other fields in which to achieve status and success.

Now, of course, enters the great clinical importance of the measurement of the relationship of phantasy to primary physical satisfaction in any of the sexual acts. Up to this time the direct physical return has not been of such a sweeping, compelling nature that it could thrust aside the language values. However, we see many children of the twelve-to-sixteen age group who can give us no account of phantasy during these acts. Our material indicates further that when the practice of masturbation, sodomy, or the like is not accompanied by phantasy, it will continue even after the age when heterosexual contacts or even marriage receive social sanction. It also indicates that boys who began their heterosexual experiences with prostitutes during adolescence, without meaningful phantasy and without deriving any return from the affairs except pleasure, afterwards look on the girls they marry solely as a means of physical satisfaction (with, of course, a bit of housekeeping thrown in). The presence of homosexual (rather than heterosexual) phantasy during erotic acts is equally prognostic.

Any previously existing mental defect or abnormality is very seriously complicated by the surge of adolescent sexuality. Disturbing examples occur with some frequency in the post-encephalitic. Such youngsters now show an irritable, restless drive that may have no sexual manifestations in the usual sense of the word, and boys of this type who come to the clinic often show a sort of gravitation towards the women in the office, though there isn't the slightest indication of a sexual approach.

In these organic cases and in the lower grades of the feeble-minded we are also accustomed to a sharp increase in delinquency or in bothersome conduct disorders at this time. My colleagues are quite at liberty to call this "sexual" behavior, though it is simpler, and perchance more useful, to look upon it as evidence of increased pressure in an area which society as well as the youngsters would have the greatest difficulty in describing as sexual. All trends towards earlier institutionalization for defective children,[9] as well as training methods that will enable them to return to the community,[10] have bearing on the subject.

During this twelve-to-sixteen-year period it is difficult for the child—particularly the boy—to fit the physical demands of sex into the demands of the society in which he lives. For instance, the boy's interest in the nude, his masturbation, his excitement in the presence of girls—all such matters seriously accentuate his growing inability to confide in the adults who have been close to him. From this point of view, public opinion in regard to the "wrongness" of the physical aspects of the sexual life affect the child. Even more potent are the waves of feeling against crimes of sex. Every few years these move to the front pages of our newspapers, where they manage to sharpen the sense of guilt and the anxiety with which the child is forced to view the normal sexual interests of his age. It takes a thoroughly impervious envelope to protect the youngster from the anathema which he is compelled to direct against his own preoccupations. I have been using the masculine here because I see this problem clearly in boys. There is no reason for assuming that it is different with girls, but it is terribly hard to get the data.

Marked individual differences exist in the effect of physical

<hr>

9 *Trends*, pp. 306–307, 673.   10 *Trends*, p. 1242.

exercise upon the sexual appetite, despite the good old stand-by of advising plenty of physical exercise as an aid in controlling the urge to masturbate. I have not kept records on this matter, but it is my impression that vigorous exercise whips up rather than allays the sexual appetite of about one in four boys. In the rest physical exercise seems to act rather effectively as a relief for sexual tension. I have no data in regard to its effect on adolescent girls.

There is an enormous amount of feeling about the effect—at this age—of "sexy" movies, burlesque shows, and so forth. A great many persons are convinced that these excite sexual interests in the physical sense. But it has been stated at various times by W. A. White that quite the opposite takes place—that spectacles of this sort drain off the sexual interests in relatively innocuous ways. So far as I know it, neither side has proof. The matter is probably of considerable importance.

Various authors, notably Havelock Ellis, have pointed out that the direct sexual drive shows itself as such much later in the girl than in the boy (according to Ellis, "A boy grows into a man; a girl has to be kissed into becoming a woman"). Thus we find it commonly pointed out that a boy's sexuality is far more easily aroused than a girl's and so must be taken into consideration in the interesting activities of the adolescent period. This is not correct. It is rather that the language components (involving a very diffuse bodily feeling of well-being and every imaginable social satisfaction) remain very high for the girl, in most cases apparently maintaining this position at least up to the time of actual sexual intercourse. To what extent this situation is social in origin, depending on the earlier status of women and likely to change with their growing economic and social equality with men, it is difficult to determine, but social trends in that direction are perhaps of importance.[11]

[11] *Trends,* Chapter XIV.

We have as yet no clear indication of the effect upon sexual appetite of the freer physical relationships between modern boys and girls. This freedom must not be thought of solely in terms of wider use of the automobile,[12] or of the fact that such relationships are worked out at a distance from neighborhood taboo, but also in terms of athletic competition, in abbreviation and "sensibleness" in dress, and so forth. The data are very conflicting. In the clinic one definitely gets the feeling that increased frankness of relationship leads to much less preoccupation with the subject —that the earlier secrecy and taboo were little more than clever invitations to constant rumination on the physical aspects of the sexual drive. On the other hand, there are indications that sexual intercourse is now more frequent among adolescents than in earlier generations.[13] However, as this last set of data is dependent upon many things besides increased frankness of relationship, the evidence is equivocal.

A matter that must be mentioned for the adolescent period is the extraordinarily wide variation in the effect of indulgence upon the sexual appetite. In some people[14] sexual expression first gives satisfaction and then leads to a negative phase in which there is a definite revulsion against further such expression; in others the appetite once aroused demands more and more by way of satisfaction.[15] Between two extremes here, there is every shade of individual reaction.

The sexual appetite is stronger during this period than at any other time (though showing more clearly from the eighteenth to

---

[12] Trends in automobile transportation (*Trends*, p. 177) and in the age at which licenses to drive cars are obtainable.

[13] *Trends*, pp. 417–418.

[14] The work with the best clinical data on this is Havelock Ellis, *Studies in the Psychology of Sex* (Philadelphia, Davis, 1929).

[15] Ellis claimed that when the orgasm was complete, the negative phase followed and inferred, even, that absence of this negative phase could be considered proof that the experience had not really been wholly satisfying. This would be difficult of proof.

the twenty-fifth year), but the social sanctions of our cultural pattern continue to be imposed against it. This points up an interesting theoretical consideration of frustration[16]—in this case imposed by society for its own good. In contrast, the body accepts signals from the organ itself when it is unwise to proceed further (e.g., nausea when the stomach is full, extreme contraction of the muscles when a bone has been broken). From the point of view of the individual's own psychophysical development it is easy to think that heterosexual outlets are far more healthy than secretive masturbation. Yet there is every sort of social pressure towards the latter. Trends in the age of marriage are important here;[17] and so are those in lessening the social load formerly carried by heterosexual intercourse.[18]

It seems too bad that as the individual moves into his adult life carrying all of the problems of this chapter, the freshest and most recent of these is to be the result of society's praise of his sexual adjustment as long as he can keep it hidden. It will be apparent in the following chapter that this is scarcely a fair statement, even though it appears to the individual himself to be so. It is fairer to put the matter in this way—that society is so anxious that the physical sexual urge be sublimated into socially useful activities that it bends its every energy towards the frustration of the actual physical expression, hoping by this means to divert that energy to other channels.[19] And at that it does a pretty efficient job.

[16] J. S. Plant, "The Social Significance of the Guidance Movement," *Mental Hygiene*, vol. 27, no. 2, pp. 268–272, particularly p. 270, April, 1943.

[17] *Trends*, p. 680.

[18] See pp. 118 f.; also *Trends*, pp. 664–679.

[19] This is one of the most striking illustrations of Frédéric Paulhan's theory of the origin and rôle of emotion. Paulhan, *The Laws of Feeling* (New York, Harcourt, 1930). This is briefly summarized in Prescott, pp. 75–76.

CHAPTER 10

The Language Values of Sexual Expression

We see children who have the problem of learning the language values of the sexual life, of learning the ways in which various needs and relationships may be expressed through these symbols, and of using them in a socially acceptable way. As already asserted in the preceding chapter most sexual phenomena have two components, though certain ones, I believe, involve no language values and others involve only language values. In the majority, in which the two components are mixed, the language values far outweigh the physical-return values.

In unraveling the tangled threads of Chapters 9 and 10 I find it helpful to use the analogy of alcoholism. Like all other analogies this is safe if not pushed too far. In the case of alcohol we speak of two reasons for drinking: the immediate physical satisfaction and the language values. It is not often that an individual drinks for only one of these reasons. However, we do know solitary drinkers and persons who "drink before breakfast"; for a high percentage of these there is apparently no more than the satisfaction from the alcohol itself. And we also know persons who dislike both the drink and its after-effect but who consume large amounts because "it's the proper thing to do" in such and such an environment. Generally speaking, however, even people who like alcohol drink only with friends, or only at the end of the day, or only to forget certain events, or only to have the feeling of being uninhibited. In other words, just as in the problem of sex, two factors are almost always present but the language or mean-

ing one is the more important.[1] The analogy can be pushed
further to the person for whom drinking has very high language
values but who may occasionally go on a spree in which there are
no language values—or *vice versa*. There are also similarities in
the problems of therapy. It is difficult to cure the person who likes
alcohol for its own sake, and correspondingly difficult to "cure"
promiscuity where there has developed a sexual life without
language values[2] (or to change the sex life of any other person for
whom physical satisfaction is the important thing).

Before entering upon the chronological development of the
problem, there are two other matters that should be mentioned,
though I have touched on them elsewhere.[3] The first is the effect
that crowded living quarters have upon the child's attitude
towards sex. The critical point is that many children witness the
sex play of older persons at a time when they, themselves, are not
mature enough to understand the language values of these activities. I study so few adults that I have no data as to what this does
to the language values of the individual's sex life as maturity arrives, but children unquestionably feel a clear disillusionment—
a stripping from the sexual acts of any meaning except that of
physical satisfaction. It is doubtful that this would seem a serious
loss to many persons under thirty, because until then the physical
returns are so intense and adequate. But it is fair to guess that
after thirty sexual life would seem much less satisfying to those
who have low language values for it. It is also fair to guess that

[1] Here, again, the question arises whether "language values" should be raised to
the level of Pareto's residues (as in my presentation) or classed as derivatives. I
feel that my formulation is, at least for the present, more realistic. See the Appendix for a full discussion of Pareto's formulation.
[2] Because promiscuity often (but by no means *always*) involves the satisfactions
discussed in Chapter 9 rather than those under consideration in the present chapter. All the education and training that the world affords will not do away with
the fact that, in terms of immediate returns, nothing equals the completed heterosexual experience.
[3] Plant, pp. 219–227, particularly p. 222.

with this group there would be a much higher incidence of promiscuity.

The second matter is the high language values that uncommon sexual practices often have for the participants. Of all of the authors who have touched upon the subject, Ellis[4] seems to me the one with the best understanding of the need that many pairs of individuals have for feeling that they "are doing something which nobody else would do." Variations of every sort are thus used to heighten the idiom of the relationship—a point completely missed by recent books on the technique of the sexual act.

The disturbances in the sexual field with which adults are chiefly concerned during the child's first five years are centered about so-called masturbation[5] and the nettling questions raised by the child. Thus a meaning—a cultural load of heavy proportions—is rapidly added to acts which usually begin by chance or by offering a direct physical satisfaction.

Masturbation in young children arises from two quite distinct sources. Thigh friction evidently gives pleasure to the child. It is prolonged among definitely retarded youngsters and occasionally among more nearly average children who are rejected at home or markedly frustrated in play outlets. Here again there is no return beyond physical satisfaction, though the fact that the activity is kept up only where other means of satisfaction are absent seems to me eloquent indication that in the normal situation the young child has little interest in sexual activities which have no language values in his society. The other source of masturbation is our adult fear of the whole business. Once we see the child rubbing the genital region, we admonish with a vigorous "no." There

[4] Havelock Ellis, *Studies in the Psychology of Sex* (Philadelphia, Davis, 1927), vol. 6, pp. 523, 531 (footnote), 544, 554.

[5] Although masturbation may produce either a soothing effect or an excitement that works towards a crisis, it is customary to use the same word in describing both phenomena. Some day social engineers will realize the great emotional loads that various words carry—and what anxiety they can arouse.

are few, if any, other activities which so early and so certainly are conditioned in terms of being the cause of acute adult disturbance. Thus the act soon carries a terrific language value—being used by the child as an attention-getting device or for any one of a host of needs in the way of fighting back against real or fancied hurts from his parents.

The fact that local irritation in the genital region (perhaps from lack of cleanliness) often induces rubbing doesn't alter the basic considerations of the above paragraphs. In some of the cases that have come to our attention masturbation has ceased with improvement of this physical condition or with circumcision. In every instance we have felt that the most important result of such intervention was the removal of language factors, which disappeared when the parents' anxiety was allayed.[6] This easement that comes to people simply from activity—regardless of its efficiency—is a constant source of wonder to the psychiatrist.[7]

It is of course difficult to know just when the physical-return components of masturbation are outweighed by the language values. However, this is not difficult to measure in the other pressing difficulty of early childhood—that of questions as to sex and the origin of babies. Unfortunately for the parents the problem very frequently has to be met at the time of pregnancy, which—for so many—has already become a period of some disturbance. This is no place to go into the intricacies of the problem of sex education—more than to say that, in our experience, what for the child is most frequently an attention-getting device, often turns out to be efficiently successful as the parents labor through an exact account of the origin of human life. It is especially so if the parents can find a psychiatrist to whom to take this child who shows "undue interest in sex." The interesting social trends here

[6] Also, in the event of circumcision, the pain following the operation furnishes a necessary break in continuity of the habit.

[7] Chester I. Barnard often speaks of the need that each of us has "to do some thing about it."

have to do with the "social propriety" of pregnancy—the extent to which style dictates that it is a period to be hidden.[8]

If the envelope, in these early years, is sieving material in terms of human relationships rather than of factual knowledge as to sex —and this has been our own belief—the problem of sex education takes an entirely new turn. Thus we are more interested in the attitude than in the data about sex that the child brings to adolescence. We are interested, above all, that it shall not become an area which disconcerts everyone and which carries a terrific load of guilt. For those parents and others who cannot discuss the subject without all sorts of emotional conflict (and there are many such, even among our best citizenry) it is much better to resurrect the shopworn story of the stork, in comfortable fashion, than to labor blushingly through the "facts" of life. All that the envelope allows the child to learn from the latter is that there is something dreadfully wrong, or dreadfully disconcerting or attention-getting, in the question he asked.

In passing it should perhaps be mentioned that the psychoanalytic group take an entirely different view from the one outlined in the previous section—namely, that the physical-return components and the language components of the sexual problem run an even race during the child's earliest years. Their dependence upon the castration complex[9] as the explanation of a great share of all human ills is evidence of this.

During the next period (roughly that of five to ten) the language factors rapidly increase in importance and spread. As with all the other problems, the child brings some of the difficulties of the earlier period into this, though he has become so accustomed

[8] *Trends,* p. 422.
[9] Healy, pp. 144 ff. This fear is postulated as striking into each one of us—the girl being sure that she has been castrated, the boy equally afraid that he will be.

to them that he has developed patterned responses. There is less doubt as to the meaning of events and less awkward experiment in expression—the envelope more accurately gauges what he can afford to receive from the outside world as well as what he is trying to convey to it.

By now, information on sexual matters has become valuable coin in buying a place with other children—because of the secrecy and taboo which surround such matters. This gives importance to comparative data on the use of dirty words in those cultural patterns where there is relatively little taboo as to sex and any trends in our own pattern towards a lessened taboo on such matters. We see discussion of masturbation, the purveying of "sexy" words, and so forth as increasingly common, during this period, among children who are having a tough time of establishing themselves in their own families, in their social group, or in school. It is most important to see these difficulties not as problems of sex but rather as problems in other relationships from which the envelope allows the child to transfer his reaction to a more dramatic field.[10]

By this time sexual information also gives its possessor prestige in terms of a feeling of being "grown up." It is this symbolic, or language, value of the information that the child finds satisfying, regardless of its accuracy or pertinence to any particular situation. We also see many children who attempt rather advanced sex play—involving very little physical satisfaction and frequently actual pain—because it carries a sense of achievement. Consequently we are interested in trends in widening or narrowing the opportunities which a given pattern offers for measuring growth.[11]

---

[10] Through this whole area the reader will find most helpful the theory of emotions expressed in Frédéric Paulhan, *The Laws of Feeling* (New York, Harcourt, 1930), p. 16. This theory, which describes emotion as arising from the thwarting of various drives and as therefore having to express itself along other lines, is a most practical basis upon which to work, regardless of some theoretical shortcomings.

[11] E.g., a pattern which very much stresses academic achievement tends to in-

My knowledge of perversions (exhibitionism, sodomy, etc.[12]) is inadequate for this age period because nearly all the patients seen at a clinic such as ours have been unwillingly or passively involved. Some can be ruled out as having participated entirely against their will; the others seem to have derived varying degrees of satisfaction from standing in with older children, imitating what they believe more sophisticated or older people do, or receiving material rewards, or to be driven by a curiosity which is not directed so much at the sexual organs themselves as towards "what older people do with these."[13] At this time sexual intercourse has a very small amount of the pleasure component unless it is repeated many times. When boys of nine or ten or a little older attempt—but cannot consummate—intercourse, the entire feeling is one of disappointment that an act symbolizing maturity couldn't be carried through rather than one of pain or tension resulting from physical frustration. This has seemed to me another indication that the language factor is larger, at this time, than that of physical satisfaction.

By five—and increasingly so as each year passes—there appears a very clear differentiation between the overt behavior of the two sexes; for though we sometimes see girls following the behavior pattern described in the previous paragraph, we see very few as compared to the number of boys. The discrepancy is the more marked in view of the fact that parents (and other guardians) are usually more insistent about bringing girls to the court or the clinic when this kind of difficulty is involved. With girls, there is a much more apparent tendency to work through the problem in

crease such use of sexual knowledge by those who cannot measure up to the accepted standard. As to these trends, see Prescott, pp. 208–209.

[12] There are many psychoanalytic case histories which record incidences of this sort in earlier life, but these are necessarily seen in retrospect at the time of the analysis. So frequently the analyst forgets that such material has more bearing on the patient's present situation than on his past life.

[13] The same values obtain for that constantly recurring group in which rites in the nature of perversions are used as initiating ceremonies for various secret clubs and societies.

terms of dispensing "information" than in terms of overt behavior. How much variations of these in pattern depend on member rôles (sociological in origin) and how much on biological differences, I don't know.

From ten to around fifteen there are much more specific physical reactions (a much sharper concentration of feeling in the
genital area), but the language factors of the psychosexual problem are still chiefly responsible for bringing these children to the
court or the clinic.

As in the earlier period a great deal of the sexual knowledge
and activity is used as an indicator of growing up. Here again
much of the sexual intercourse of this period is dominated by an
unpleasant (or even painful) rather than pleasant tone. Children
give us this description until they have had a number of such experiences.

We adults live in perpetual amazement at the evident "sexual"
behavior of members of this age group, at their preoccupation
with this problem—with so little realization of the import it has
for the youngsters themselves. A recent tendency in psychiatric
literature to unmask all such activity would have been more
realistic if it had recognized the two components of the problem.
All through life the various sexual phenomena will be used as a
means of expressing relationships that seem to be beyond the individual's verbal mode of communication, and during this ten-to-
sixteen age period we are seeing the ataxic, stumbling early lessons
in this most important of matters. There is no area of companionship so rich in communication through the psychomotor tensions—unless it be the cuddling, enveloping activities of the
mother in the child's first few weeks. So, from now on, sex becomes the medium through which in most intense, most accurate,
and most subtle fashion one person talks to another.

Once more, the acts and the accompanying phantasy are of clini-

cal importance in that they provide an important means of measuring the heterosexual drive and interest. But even more important is the phantasy—since, as pointed out,[14] the same acts at
different times or under different conditions may have entirely
different meanings. The envelope acts here to give to each individual entirely idiomatic connotations for quite identical oc-
currences.[15]

One of the pressing problems of the ten-to-sixteen age group is
that of girls to whom sexual experiences mean that they are
cared for as individuals—as themselves. We earlier mentioned
the stubborn fact that many second-raters find in sex an area in
which they are "as good as any one else,"[16] but this is not quite
what is meant here. Children, in growing up, are forever being
held to certain standards; they so often exist only in terms of set-
up goals. As girls mature these can magically disappear; they are
wanted for themselves for something for which no standard has
been built. For a society interested in confining sexual intercourse within marital bounds this is not a pleasant situation. It
points up once more the great importance of broadening the base
of success for children,[17] since there is less compulsion to turn to
the sexual field for children who are finding satisfaction in other
ways.

Sometimes we see sexual experiences (particularly intercourse)
used as a measure of social success in competition. Here there is a
frank discussion of what persons or what number of persons one
"makes," just as there is gossip about school marks or new clothes.
There are also factors of physical satisfaction—of that I am sure.
But these are secondary to the number of achievements that can

---

[14] See pp. 118 f.

[15] E.g., sodomy may "mean" complete satisfaction of a homosexual urge and tie
or an equally gratifying substitute for heterosexual needs that will be satisfied as
soon as social codes allow.

[16] Chapter 9, p. 121.

[17] There are many such trends. An example of a trend towards narrowing this
base appears in *Trends*, p. 303.

be advertised. One can't clearly separate the two components, except in experiences which are almost completely made up of one or the other. If it is noised about that Mary has had relations with a number of boys, then John's interest in "making" her is perhaps in part that he cannot be outdone by his peers and perhaps in part that he hopes to find an easy answer to his needs for physical satisfaction—and no one, not even John, can accurately fractionate the incident. We have seen two situations, however, in which large groups attempted such public and accurate tally of these affairs that no one could doubt that competition quite outweighed physical gratification.

From fifteen on the teasing apart of the factors of this chapter and the preceding one becomes increasingly difficult. As we have earlier indicated,[18] the last three or four generations have given to sexual intercourse a tremendous value in its own right. It has been very largely freed from the heavy sociological burden it so long carried. Perhaps this is the reason for our present psychiatric interest in it, including the building of a whole theory of behavior around its tensions. This has been unfortunate to the extent that it has eclipsed the part that the various sexual acts play as a mode of communication—a part which they are now freer to play. Those psychiatrists who loudly affirm that the mother cannot falsify in the field of belongingness as she cuddles her child, would do well to recognize that husbands and wives (and other interested parties) cannot falsify in the field of belongingness as they engage in the more intimate aspects of the sexual relationship. One hopes that this view will spread before the present crop of authors on the subject of techniques in the sexual field turn their talents to books addressed to mothers on the various techniques to be used in fondling and cuddling their babies.

[18] See pp. 120 f.

CHAPTER 11

Temperament

We see children who have the problem of keeping a workable and comfortable balance between the various forces driving towards extraversion or introversion. As it seems to be more or less agreed that this matter of temperament is in some way a function of certain physical factors within the individual, one might question the importance of social pressures in this area. But two matters cannot be ignored: (1) that the crowding together of people and the increasing complexity of their inter-dependence create serious stresses for the extraverted individual; (2) that a highly developed civilization forces introversion of a traumatic sort upon each of its members. Millions of people living at close quarters must behave as though they were introverted if the whole affair is not to be a madhouse.

I confess that I must beg the question whether there are marked changes in the actual temperament of any given person, but I am sure that there appear to be such changes as the individual meets varying social pressures. Usually these fluctuations in temperament remain in a relatively narrow band of the whole scale—a band in which the individual habitually moves.[1] In quite the same way, a stream shows differences in width and speed of flow as it passes different sorts of terrain. Recent experience has confirmed my faith in the theory, stated in an earlier volume,[2] that extraversion and introversion function in the same area.[3] On this

1 Plant, p. 111.   2 Plant, pp. 109–115.
3 So careful a group of workers as those associated with H. A. Murray feel that my formulation is not acceptable (*Explorations in Personality*, London, Oxford University Press, 1939), but do not seem to me to give adequate reasons for their objections.

basis the problem of temperament is expressed in terms of freedom or constriction of the individual's mental attributes and
drives[4] rather than in terms of his being an extravert or an introvert.[5] I have no proof of what the barrier may be, but I assume
a physicochemical relationship to the motor pathways.

The envelope and the wall of status preservation also function
in this area, but by means of different mechanisms.[6] Admittedly,
if a child appears at the clinic with a particularly impervious envelope, a marked degree of introversion, or a very thick and high
wall of status preservation (or the opposites of these three), it is a
difficult matter to make a differential diagnosis. But between
these extremes the barriers are quite different. Whereas the envelope translates on the sensory level, temperament controls expression on the motor level and affects the envelope only to the
extent that as it slows up expression it allows the envelope to
function more efficiently. The relationship between traumatic
introversion and the wall of status preservation is discussed below.[7]

This matter of temperament is one of transcending social importance because civilization is, among other things, a process
that thwarts and redirects raw drives—an introverting force of
considerable magnitude. Though there is evidence to the effect
that the more healthy personal adjustment is that representing a
mild degree of extraversion, in our culture the extraverted one is,
on every hand, the disadvantaged soul; he is the nuisance in the
family, the problem child in school, the delinquent. How can we
crowd closer together, develop ever more intricate human rela-

[4] Fritz Künkel's formulation of the internal and external dialectic is a different
way of expressing much the same thing. See *Character, Growth, Education* (Philadelphia, Lippincott, 1938), pp. 1–63, and especially pp. 64–72.

[5] If these words are used to describe ways in which a person behaves rather than
to define types of people, the difficulties of Jung's earlier formulation are largely
overcome.

[6] See also Chapter 3.   [7] See pp. 139, 146.

tionships—and continue to put up with the bouncy, expansive extravert?

Clinically one may suspect an inherent as well as a traumatic form of introversion, but the two often merge and cannot be distinguished except by treatment. Given a daydreaming, shut-in child, only the test of therapy will reveal to what extent his withdrawal is of traumatic origin—the result of repeated rebuffs and defeats in social contacts. That is, as we attempt to move the temperament towards the pole of extraversion, we come, sooner or later, to a point beyond which we can't seem to go. For the residual introversion I have used the word "inherent," but whether it is inherited in the ordinary sense I haven't the slightest idea. What seems important is that in psychiatric practice there is a general desire to shift patients away from the introversion end of temperament adjustment, and that in actual practice one finds a point beyond which present-day therapeutic procedures seem futile.

On the basis that introversion is the imposed or thwarting condition, one obviously could not speak of "traumatic extraversion." It is true that certain drugs (notably alcohol) produce such a state temporarily; certain psychotic states (notably the manic-depressive psychoses) do the same. But it is our experience that with the ordinary, "normal" shifts in temperament, social pressures effectively operate only in the direction of introversion. Such a view would rather assume that extraversion is the original, or natural, temperament, and there are some bits of data to support this view.[8]

Certainly all babies at birth appear to be extraverted, since

[8] It isn't fair to claim support from authors who have approached the problem from an entirely different angle. Thus I can merely point out that the concept of the viscerotonic as the most natural temperament does not conflict with the view just expressed. See W. H. Sheldon and S. S. Stevens, *The Varieties of Temperament* (New York, Harper, 1942), Chapter v, particularly pp. 256, 257.

even those of definitely introverted stocks respond directly and immediately to stimuli. But heredity must play some part in temperament, for we see children following the adjustment pattern of their own stock even when brought up from babyhood by families of entirely different temperament. Climate must also play a rôle, since there is a very definite tendency towards increased introversion among groups as they live farther from the equator. However, this factor seems to have long-range rather than short-range importance, since children from warm climates retain their tendency to extraversion if brought up in temperate or colder zones. Certainly the glands of internal secretion also play a rôle in temperament, even if we don't understand too well what it is.[9] Two areas of research open here. The first involves the relationship of individual endocrine glands to temperament. The second involves the complicated relationship of the various glands to one another. Finally, one gets the impression that certain children have internal resources to a marked degree[10]—with the question still unanswered as to how much of this is congenital. Here one feels that the clinical picture of introversion is dependent upon a richness and fullness of the mental life which mean that the child is alone because he doesn't seem to need others rather than because he can't get along with others. There are some interesting trends here in children's toys—toys which invite the child's cooperation or management as opposed to toys that "do all the going themselves."[11]

From birth till around five the child moves towards that band of temperament adjustment in which he will continue. This "band" is much affected by, but probably not determined by, the considerations of the previous section. There are many factors involved during this preschool adjustment.

[9] One gets a fascinating vista of this all through W. H. Sheldon and S. S. Stevens (*op. cit.*).
[10] Chapter 7.
[11] J. C. Foster and M. L. Mattson, *Nursery-School Education* (New York, Appleton-Century, 1939), Chapter XIV.

Some of these are: (1) The number of available playmates. When the number isn't adequate, we see children (a) quite satisfactorily playing by themselves; (b) associating much with their parents or with children several years older, so that the relationship is still a child-parent one; (c) "hanging around with nothing to do"; or (d) retiring into phantasy life. Of course, the key word here is "available"—if the child has some marked precocity or defect, others who happen to be of the same chronological age may not be available in the sense that they offer anything like fair or interesting competition. The important trends are those in birth rate,[12] in roaming range,[13] in movement to suburbs, where houses are farther apart,[14] and in growth of nursery schools.[15]

(2) Countless thwarting experiences with older or more favored siblings or playmates. This is an important matter, which has not been given adequate weight as the trends towards smaller families and suburban living have sharply cut into the easy play outlets for children. As noted above, the increased roaming range and the development of nursery schools constitute trends in the opposite direction. I am sure, however, that the traumatic introversion which gets its start from the rebuffs of older children or from the absence of an inviting play environment during these early years often plays a part all the way through life. This sort of experience results in much the same clinical picture as situations in which the introversion is inherent, though obviously a quiet but persistent provision of satisfactory outlets will change the former where it won't the latter.

(3) Certain parental situations—as, for instance, those in which there are dominating or overly executive types of parents. Out of this one sees two general types of reaction. Some children, though giving a general impression of shy introversion, find various effective modes of asserting themselves or their position (enuresis is a good example). Other children completely crumple under

12 *Trends,* pp. 31–43.   13 *Trends,* pp. 172–176.
14 *Trends,* pp. 11–17.   15 *Trends,* p. 788.

situations of this kind, presenting absolutely nothing that can be recognized as rebellion.

(4) Various sorts of self-centering experiences. Perhaps the most common of these is illness,[16] so that we are interested in trends in the frequency and severity of chronic diseases in children.[17] Certainly braces, casts, supports, and so forth, act in much the same way. Matters of this kind play their part well in developing traumatic introversion. In these early years this usually takes the form of retreat into phantasy life or the use of various substitute ways of gaining social recognition, such as attention-getting devices or disorders involving lying or stealing for prestige (rather than merely for self-protection or from cupidity).

From five to twelve certain factors operating for or against the adjustment the child has made place a maximum burden upon the envelope. Some examples of the stresses will illustrate. To a very marked degree the school experience is one that favors introversion. We have known for some time that nearly all whom the teachers consider problem children follow an extraverted pattern.[18] While there are very definite and quite exciting trends towards a change in attitude,[19] it will be a long time before approval swings away from children who sit quietly with relatively little physical expression of the rich mental life of these years. The shift in emphasis has largely affected the earlier grades. The development of vocational training at the high school level has been a step in the same direction, but the regular academic high school set-up still favors the quiet, self-contained individual.

16 So often we see a successfully piloted physical convalescence which hasn't in the slightest degree involved the equally important matter of "turning the interests out again." We find such children now physically fit but presenting a perfectly typical picture of introversion because of a prolonged period of being cut off from all interests except that of their own symptoms and autism.

17 *Trends*, pp. 757–761.

18 E. K. Wickman, *Children's Behavior and Teachers' Attitudes* (New York, Commonwealth Fund, 1928).

19 Prescott, pp. 219–220.

In Essex County (which is probably typical of urban areas throughout the country) there is an overscheduling of children's lives. The whole matter is all mixed up with the problem of integration.[20] In an effort to supervise their recreation and to meet the competitive demands of the cultural pattern, youngsters are given this or that "lesson" or are urged to join this or that organization,[21] which takes up an increasing amount of their time outside of school and we see them hurrying along to keep up with their schedules.[22] A number of children persistently run away— seeking thus to find a life which is in their own hands. It is this sort of experience that leads us to say that scheduling, compressing experience puts the temperament under stress—with the explosive runaway episodes as a result whenever the envelope cannot sufficiently protect the child from the need of the environment to press its claims upon his development.

The movies and the radio are perhaps the most dramatic and omnipresent of a large number of amusements which require (or even allow) little physical participation on the part of the child. The older psychiatrist has little difficulty in imagining the dire prognostications of dementia praecox that would have been made thirty years ago, if we had then known of the hours that children would spend sitting fairly quietly while taking in through eyes or ears the rich emotional material involved in these affairs.[23] The best study of the effect of the movies was that carried out under the auspices of the Payne Fund.[24]

Finally there is the whole complex of situations and pressures

20 Chapter 7.
21 The fact that many of these interests involved extraverted types of activity does not vitiate the point of this paragraph—namely, that the scheduling itself works in just the opposite direction.
22 The trends in these extracurricular activities, children's organizations, riding lessons, music lessons, supervised play, etc., are given in *Trends*, pp. 788–792.
23 Trends in the development of all such activities appear in *Trends*, pp. 790–791.
24 The best reference here is Young, p. 628—where there is a good bibliography on the entire subject. The Payne Fund Studies are listed under the name of H. Blumer, who directed them.

that have come out of social congestion. Crowding in cities has limited contact with the soil and water; and owing to lack of play space, it has sharply curtailed the chance for free physical expression.[25] The trends that are important are those in urbanization,[26] those in the development of playgrounds, parks, swimming pools, and so forth[27] and those in the growth of such decentralizing forms of power as electricity and chemical sources of energy.[28]

The period of adolescence (roughly twelve to eighteen) seems to emphasize the temperament—swinging the extravert towards more extraversion, the introvert towards more introversion. The former quite commonly shows more bouncy and out-going symptoms, the latter more dreaminess and symbolic types of behavior. It is not clear whether this emphasis is based on some fairly definite change in body chemistry or merely on the fact that the vulnerability and unsettlement of adolescence bring out the eccentric, but it does not seem very important from the point of view of behavior or of the envelope's function in protecting the child from environmental pressures. In the psychiatric field, however, we are accustomed to seeing rather typical pictures of early schizophrenia during these middle teens—in youngsters who spontaneously return to their earlier temperament as the period closes (roughly some two out of three or four out of five show this clearing up). We have no data on the ability of these "early praecoxes" to stand severe emotional crises later in life; we only know that through their early twenties they seem to be making adequate adjustments. It is always inviting to turn to analogies in fields less complex. Thus one can think of those who move at some distance from the usual average balance in temperament as slipping fur-

---

[25] I have discussed this in various places. Perhaps the best place to start is at the reference given above—namely, Plant, pp. 109–115.
[26] *Trends*, p. 448.   [27] *Trends*, pp. 914–921.
[28] *Trends*, pp. 139–141.

ther away during the stormy period of adolescence—as though
the difficulty lay in clinging somewhere near the median line. At
the close of the period of sexual maturation, in the majority of
cases decreasing physical tension seems to allow the individual to
pull his temperament back towards the average. With some, however, this basic "orthotendency" isn't strong enough to accomplish the task of reintegration, so that we see the beginning of one
or the other of the great functional psychoses (dementia praecox
or manic-depressive insanity). But we should not go too far here,
even though it is possible to think of these psychoses as exaggera-
tions of the temperament. This is not meant to say that these two
groups of illness are dysfunctions of the temperament; but rather
that ill individuals express such maladjustment in one or the
other way on the basis of the original temperament. Oversimplification leads one to say that these two forms of breakdown are
less well described as two different diseases than as the illness of
two different persons.

For the considerations of this section it is difficult to set out
specific important social trends. It seems obvious that there
should be, for each person, some sort of parallel between his own
development and the social demands or opportunities that press
upon him—the whole problem of cadence.[29] We speak rather
glibly of "faster living," of children "doing things earlier in life
than we used to," or of a "lengthening of adolescence in the social
sense"; but these are not easy to measure.

There is, however, one matter that requires its own paragraph
—the instability that appears in most girls during the six to eight
months just prior to the establishment of menstruation. This is
not easy to describe, though the clinician finds that the problems
discussed in this section seem to be even more marked during that
period. Workers in the field of conduct disorders find it much

29 Chapter 6.

more difficult to develop or maintain rapport with a youngster at this period than a few months earlier or later. Even when a girl has no foreknowledge of what is about to occur, there is a certain pervasive tension as though she sensed that "something important is going to happen." It is more than possible that the basis of this is physical—that it represents on a grand scale the piling up of physical tensions that we see in miniature just before each menstrual period in the adult. Obviously this would give importance to trends in the age at which menstruation begins. I don't know of reliable data in this area.

As most children come to the close of adolescence an effort is made (as mentioned above) at pulling back the temperament towards the central line. This is beyond the ability of certain individuals. Moreover, our own cultural pattern makes this more difficult for the extraverted than for the introverted groups. We have already enumerated a number of examples of these pressures. In addition to these there is the presence of a selective heredity—that civilization tends always to make it difficult for the extravert to grow up, marry, bring up children. The introverting process of civilization might work its way through in far more rapid fashion were it not that the very nature of the extravert means that he is precisely the one who does grow up and does tend to have a more active heterosexual life. Also there are the pressures that now come definitely into their own, the trends towards the substitution of symbols for reality (e.g., words for experience, money for goods).

So the individual goes on into adult life—with his temperament adjustment fairly well established but never with any peace as to its fitting into the demands and opportunities of his environment, which at each moment invites him to be so much more the introvert or so much more the extravert. By this time he has become a more or less full-blown schizophrenic, a ritual-loving and rather implastic "normal," or a vivacious "normal" who throws himself wholeheartedly into each environmental situation that appears, or he swings like a weathervane, helplessly between imprudent exaltation and heavy depression.

Or something between any two of these.

CHAPTER 12

Reaction to Failure

We see children who have the problem of adjusting to "failure"—a word that covers situations in which the environment presents an impasse to the personality in one or another persistent or overwhelming way, as well as situations in which there are serious threats to the personality or one of its important parts.[1] But this definition has dangerous pitfalls. It must separate out what we deal with in this chapter from those multitudinous blocks which every day, for every person, force a raw drive to be turned to a substitute mode of expression that is socially acceptable. If one uses "thwart" for the latter phenomenon, then the difference between the two is quantitative rather than qualitative. This certainly entails a wide middle zone, where it would be difficult to say whether we deal with thwarts or failures. Moreover, the extent of this middle zone differs for different individuals and for each individual on different days.

I find it most practical to follow Paulhan's theory that emotion develops out of the thwarting of one or another drive[2] and is thus always the result of frustration. The energy so released provides the means for carrying out more socially acceptable behavior. For instance, if the child is hungry and the parent says he may eat if he washes his face, the resulting nudge towards cleanliness has probably not irreparably damaged the child's ego—even

[1] This book does not deal with the problem of personality disintegration—I hope to record our experiences with this at some other time.

[2] For an excellent discussion of this in the setting of other theoretical formulations, see Prescott, pp. 75–81. Paulhan uses the term "drive" for my "problem," but for this part of the discussion the two words are synonymous. He assumes fewer drives and that they are in some way an inherent trait of tissue growth.

though failure (in this instance, I should use the term "thwart") was involved for the moment in the sense that he was not allowed to eat as soon as he wished. With such a view failure is a valuable experience up to a certain point. Most of these social frustrations are converted by the envelope into something which is not catastrophic to the personality. This translation of raw drives or needs into socially acceptable action is perhaps the most pervasive and common dynamism in the whole process of social growth or civilization.[3] However, the matter does not always work out in this way for the individual; there are times when an acceptable answer to the blocking seems to be not only beyond realization but beyond hope. Perhaps the envelope has not adequately "softened" the initial frustration; perhaps the internal constellation of abilities or the *Gestalt* of the "problems" cannot conform to the demands upon it (in other words, it is not ready for the experience to which it is exposed); perhaps the emotion aroused is so intense that it is disintegrating rather than energizing. In such instances, I use the word "failure" rather than "thwart."

Failure may involve any or all of the twenty-one problems of this book and in various degrees. It may break in upon the individual with brusque and overwhelming force, or work quite as effectively in subtle but long-drawn fashion. Rather definite types of reaction on the child's part show themselves as the pressure becomes more than he can stand, regardless of the conditions given in the previous sentence. These reactions tend to appear at certain age levels, some to remain through life, others to be replaced by reactions characteristic of a later age. It is possible that the type of personality plays a part in the choice and permanency

[3] For the last twenty years a voluble group has been pointing out the devastating results of our repression of sexual interests and activities among young people (in disappointing comparison with the absence of anxieties in this field in such places as the South Sea Islands). They forget that, according to Paulhan, this repression is one of the most important factors in the rapid growth of our civilization. It is not my present purpose to champion one or the other of these situations—but only to point out that everything is bought at a price.

of the reaction.[4] I have assumed it more probable that the development of different reactions represents a function of maturity, and that the individual maintains a certain mode instead of turning to a new one only when it has seemed adequately to hide his defeat. Given the views in this chapter and those in our brief discussion of the latest established reflex as the one showing emotional problems,[5] it seems evident that what the child does under stress is perhaps far more dependent on what he is than on what caused the stress. This is one of the most difficult things for the clinician to learn. The tying of the "symptom" to the type of person and his age is quite as important in the field of conduct as in the physical field.

One can suppose that the problem is first met at birth—in the decidedly uncomfortable character of that event. Even if the child cannot consciously formulate the matter, there is a good deal of clinical data[6] which indicates that this event impresses on him in some deep way the notion that very terrible things can occur and that he has no recourse. Therefore, while we are not able to outline the ways in which the child reacts in the first hours to the catastrophe of birth, we are still interested in trends in injuries received at birth and in developments towards easing the process of birth.[7] At best, it would seem, the affair remains very critical for one who has known nothing but well-fed comfort. The novelty of the experiences that follow (helplessness, cold, hunger, pains, etc.) certainly reinforces the birth-trauma factors, and there are correspondingly important trends in antepartum clinics, well-child conferences, and so forth.[8]

[4] The interesting assumption that various symptom-complexes are not manifestations of different diseases, but of the same disease in different people, is appearing more frequently in the literature.
[5] See pp. 119, 120.
[6] Used by Otto Rank in the development of his theory of the trauma of birth.
[7] White House Conference, p. 67, summarizes this.
[8] *Loc. cit.*

From early babyhood (sometimes even from the second or third day) many children feel the lack of security.[9] These are what we term "rejected" children.[10] Children's reactions are pretty much the same (panic, anxiety, loss of morale, or regression) whatever the reason for rejection, but we distinguish three main sources: (1) The situation in which the mother has always rejected her rôle as a woman and so rejects the child[11] as a symbol of this.[12] (2) The situation in which parents recognize that the child threatens their mutual relationship. This may appear, for instance, if the child comes too early in the marriage or on top of serious physical or financial problems; if the child absorbs the interest of one mate and thus arouses jealousy; or if the child is of the wrong sex to fulfill the family dreams. (3) The situation in which total rejection begins with rejection of one trait. That is, when the child looks, or speaks, or behaves like a person who has been the family black sheep or a person whom the family has always detested, a process starts which feeds upon itself, to come before us with all the classical symptoms of a full-blown rejection—and with just as many difficulties to clear up.[13] In other words, the tension that the child's trait sets off in the adult begets tension in the child leading to more adult disapproval, and so on.

Precisely these same problems are raised by desertion or by the

[9] Chapter 1.

[10] For the four components of rejection, see p. 11.

[11] Obviously in this situation girls are more often and more seriously rejected than boys.

[12] So that trends in the changing status of women are of importance. These appear at least in terms of economic and social self-sufficiency (*Trends*, Chapter xiv) and the importance society gives to the bearing and rearing of children (*Trends*, pp. 51–56). I am sure, also, that the development of any sort of population policy will have a profound effect here; perhaps the best recent coverage of this area, *Population Roads to Peace or War*, by G. I. Burch and Elmer Pendell (Washington, Population Reference Bureau, 1945).

[13] It's perfectly possible that this third "cause" is only a subheading of one of the other two—that the rejection was there to begin with and only crystallized about a trait. We all dislike certain traits in our children, and it may be that here we see why in certain instances this grows to full-blown rejection, whereas, of course, in most instances it does not.

child's inadvertent discovery that he has been adopted, but such events tend to affect him later (say, after the age of five), whereas rejection by his own parents within the family circle, as already pointed out, is felt even in the first days of life. The clinical picture differs in that, besides exhibiting the usual symptoms,[14] the child definitely attempts to punish the offending adult (making trouble for or stealing from him or her) or the adults whom he identifies with the offender. Prevailing social attitudes in regard to desertion, divorce, and adoption are important here, as well as the statistical trends.[15]

From the age of two, the child faces the problem of attaining adequacy[16] (or, as the psychoanalytic group put it, adjusting to inferiority).[17] Although the problem is intensified when he begins to come in contact with outsiders, it certainly appears in family life though the latter is dedicated to the attainment of security. As the child is compared with siblings and other children in the clan family, his responses begin to follow the inadequacy pattern, in which overcompensations and bullying predominate ("I am not a failure; I will find someone weaker than I, and then I will be a success"). The important and interesting trends in this field are those in the development of standardized measurements of children, weight charts, intelligence scales, and so forth,[18] and those in the growth of nursery schools for very young children (again inviting comparisons with peers).[19]

---

[14] See p. 11.

[15] *Trends*, pp. 416–417, 688–693. A full discussion of social and legal aspects of divorce and separation (including an article of my own containing a number of case studies) appears in *Law and Contemporary Problems: Children of Divorced Parents* (Durham, Duke University School of Law, 1944), vol. 10, no. 5.

[16] Chapter 14. This whole section may be looked upon as the obverse of the problem of developing adequacy.

[17] The psychoanalytic group (with a somewhat different development of the theme) has recognized the importance of this problem in the inferiority complex (inferiority feelings being ascribed to failure "to achieve the wishes connected with the Oedipus situation"). See Healy, p. 370.

[18] *Trends*, pp. 795–798.   [19] *Trends*, p. 788.

Sometimes from the age of three or four a child will have a sense of individual failure because he is a member of a racial or religious minority.[20] Here there is a new and difficult complexity that arises out of the need that the child has to punish those very parents who give him security because it is they who determine his status. Therefore trends in social tolerance are important.[21] as are also those in the general acceptance of organized religious credos.[22]

Somewhere in these very tender years children seem to sense certain organ inferiorities, though they may not be able to verbalize their feelings. One of the startling experiences of our work is this "unconscious" appreciation on the part of a four-or-five-year-older of his inability to compete physically with his peers. He comes to us as the shy one or the sissy, but we often find that the root of the matter is poor coordination or a weak heart or other organ, for which the child has created a protective device. It is hard to determine, and perhaps not too important, whether his regressive behavior represents a persistence of the insecurity pattern or an attempt to bully his parents ("I will continue to hold my sway over them"). The significant trends are those emphasizing the rôle of allergies, bad teeth, faulty bone growth, and so forth[23] and trends in the amelioration of such conditions (rickets is perhaps the best example).[24]

As early as four the envelope allows children to recognize that they are "not liked" by others, that they are shunned as being mean or unfair. I am in some trouble about my data here, as I have no idea how many of the children who are unpopular with their peers (say at the kindergarten level) don't realize this. It is rarely that such a child is referred. However, in visiting kinder-

---

[20] This is discussed more fully in Chapters 1 and 13. The important consideration here is the "unreasonable" nature of the problem—that it obviously has nothing in it which the child or his parents could have obviated.

[21] *Trends,* pp. 600–601—summarizing Chapter XI.

[22] *Trends,* pp. 397–414.   [23] *Trends,* pp. 645–650.

[24] *Trends,* pp. 603 ff., 1061–1062.

gartens one does see outsiders who are never chosen but who seem completely oblivious to social ostracism.

At about the same time (i.e., the age of four) certain children begin to meet the problem of inability to play—awkwardness, slow maturing of reflexes, solemn lack of "spirit of play," and so forth. The trends of importance are those in the field of recreation—in the growth of competitive games,[25] in the individualization of recreation with "tutoring in play," and in the concept of recreation as an individual release.

By four another very important aspect of the problem presents itself in the special matter of the absence of near-by playmates of suitable age and physical or mental maturation. There are several important trends here—those in the birth rate,[26] those in the roaming range of young children (the automobile plays an important part),[27] those in moving from crowded cities to suburban areas,[28] and those in nursery school facilities.[29] Again the point is that if a certain number of available playmates seems to be a good thing (or even a "necessity"), then a sweeping social trend towards a larger or a smaller number is as important as any other factor.

Because it appears so frequently elsewhere, I need only mention here the pervasiveness of the problem of school failure beginning at five and running through the next eleven years. Our civilization gives a thorough training in class consciousness—each child knows the ages of his classmates to the exact month. The trends in broadening the base of promotion and of the development of special classes (as I have so frequently said) are of importance here.

[25] *Trends*, pp. 925–934, deals with this, but chiefly in relation to adults. One can get quite disturbed over the growing interest and drive in the physical education field towards having all school children develop a competitive spirit.

[26] *Trends*, p. 38.   [27] *Trends*, pp. 172–176.

[28] *Trends*, p. 456.   [29] *Trends*, p. 788.

By six or seven the family's material possessions and social position begin to have consequence to the child. The trends of importance here are those in class consciousness,[30] those in reliance on symbols (money, clothes, etc.) as establishing success,[31] and those in school consolidation tending to throw together children of markedly different family background.[32] A year or so later the inadequacy problems involved in minority race situations begin to appear. These are covered in Chapter 13.

As the child moves into adolescence—as he continues to work out the difficulties discussed in the previous sections or to carry the scars of earlier defeats—he may show the reactions of insecurity and inadequacy or may retreat into daydreams ("I am not a failure; I will find a world in which I am a success").[33] The latter response is the one which sometimes appears before adolescence and which frequently runs into adult years.

The essentially adult reactions are three: (1) That of raising a new issue—of drawing a red herring across the trail ("I am not a failure; I would be a success if it were not for . . ."). But denials of failure are not strictly accurate, as in each case the individual is beset with his inability to meet certain issues. Moreover, in such instances he will rapidly "confess" his failure if he is approached with any sort of sympathetic understanding. This is the psychoneurosis of the adult, which has indeed been anticipated in the child's awareness that something is wrong. (2) That of accepting failure—of accepting defeat. The vagrant and the beggar

[30] R. S. Lynd and Helen Lynd, *Middletown in Transition* (New York, Harcourt, 1937) in many places. Consult the excellent index.

[31] *Trends*, Chapter XVII—references occur throughout the chapter. It is hard to state the idea statistically.

[32] *Trends*, p. 1019.

[33] There is also overcompensation—noisiness from the littlest one, the loudest clothes from the poorest one, angry elbowing from the least advantaged, the calling of the police by the least secure.

come to mind—but among one's neighbors are many less dramatic examples of a rather abject acceptance of the overwhelming pressures of reality. While children's bully reactions and daydreaming are bothersome, at least they are attempts at doing something about situations which adults too often merely accept. (3) That of accepting failure—on the basis of having some other avenue of success ("I do not make enough money, but I stand high in my profession"). As we have used the terms, this might be called a reaction to thwarting rather than failure; or with some juggling, a variation of the reaction to failure. In clinic work it is simpler to see it as a separate type of reaction.

There is a special problem arising out of the question whether repeated and serious failure (inferiority) can finally develop those symptoms typical of insecurity rather than those of inadequacy. This question whether one can "break the spirit" of the bully, to produce the panicky picture of the insecure person, is one of great importance. I believe that the answer is "yes" and that occasionally I have seen its occurrence as early as ten years. The problem is affected by the magnitude and catholicity of financial fluctuations[34] and by trends in unemployment.[35] It is equally affected by trends in other fields of interpersonal competition (appearance, recreation, sports, etc.), but the latter are extremely difficult to measure.

[34] *Trends,* pp. 433–435.   [35] *Trends,* p. 779.

CHAPTER 13

Minority Race Problems

We see children who have to meet the problem of belonging to a minority race. The sociological fractions of this problem are of tremendous complexity and have been dealt with extensively by other writers. In no part of the whole field of personality adjustment is the individual more helpless, and from no source are there more pressures on the envelope.

The cultural aspects of this problem are perhaps outside the field of the present discussion, but there are at least six considerations that have important bearing on it. (1) The number and size of the minority groups in any pattern. A single Negro family living in a white community has a very different problem of adjustment from one living where there are enough other Negro families to make everyone conscious of racial matters as a community problem. (2) The cultural strength of any or all such groups. Where a minority group has cohesion and a structure of its own the problem for each member is not the same as where each family is more or less "on its own," though the set-ups are of comparable magnitude. (3) The economic threat of the minority group in question. The issues become sharper for each individual as his group attains some sort of economic equality with the majority group. (4) The parallel rise of minority groups and "decay" of majority groups. The sense of growing towards (2) and (3) is of enormous importance in sharpening the issues involved for each person. However, as I have repeatedly pointed out, change is not so important as the speed of change—acceleration. (5) The strength of any particular minority group in communities or other patterns than the one under consideration. A simple example constantly comes to mind in our work—the sharpening of a racial issue in one of our communities stirs all the neighboring ones. (6) The relationship in color or stock between the minority and the majority group. Other things being equal (only they never are), the issues are much more acute for a Negro in a community where the majority are Anglo-Saxon than for an Italian in the same community.

There is also certainly a problem of belonging to a majority race—only we know practically nothing about it. It seems as if persons who create feelings of insecurity and inadequacy must be affected quite as much by the phenomenon as are those in whom they create these attitudes,[1] but up to the present time we simply do not have the clinical data to illuminate the point. It has been very tempting in these last years to look to Germany for the answers. However, certain majority groups in areas much nearer home present quite different clinical pictures.

There are no more intricate problems in the whole range of personality adjustments than are involved in this matter of minority-race status. Two pairs of different but symbiotic mechanisms are constantly mingled in inextricable confusion.[2]

In the first pair each member of a minority race is constantly faced with all the social and economic frustrations of the group as a whole, which means that in everything that he desires or plans he must take into consideration a certain extra hazard arising out of his racial status. ("If someone says 'yes' or 'no,' my first thought is that 'it's because I am a Jew.'") On the other hand, this same consideration provides a welcome relief from personal responsibility. Nothing is one's fault but rather the fault that he belongs

[1] This is the subject of "The Toll of Intolerance upon the Intolerant," by D. M. Levy, in *The Family in a World at War*, S. M. Gruenberg, editor (New York, Harper, 1942). Some of the more intense aspects of the problem are clearly outlined on pages 117–124.

[2] Bruno Lasker in *Race Attitudes in Children* (New York, Holt, 1929) approaches this whole subject from a very different standpoint but his book has the great value of direct quotation from innumerable children. The reader will find there poignant illustration of my approach as well as Lasker's.

to a minority group. The literature on the subject has not given adequate recognition to the fact that the situation inhibits the impulse to change or growth. If I am a member of a majority group and I am unpopular—I have only myself to blame, I am pretty strongly driven to do something about *myself*. If I am a member of a minority group and I am unpopular—I need do nothing about myself or even consider that my traits or actions are of any importance in the matter. When someone says of a bit of behavior, "That's the way all Mexicans act," he shackles the individual with fetters that are as heavy as they are unfair, but he also sets him free. That person who, in any given difficulty, can even approximate how much the minority race factor is a cause and how much an excuse is indeed wise. These two apparently opposite tendencies have a reciprocal relationship, each feeding on the other to strengthen itself.

In the second pair of mechanisms the matter of belonging to a minority race confronts the individual at two different times and in two quite different ways. Yet here, again, are reciprocal support and aggravation. Later in this chapter it will appear that I have rather definitely dated these two confrontations, but in actual life little more can be said than that certainly one starts before the other and that soon the two are chaotically mingled. The first confrontation of this second pair of mechanisms is characterized by unreasonableness. The child very early finds himself in a situation for which he cannot possibly have an answer— about which in the widest stretch of imagination he could have done nothing. The chance of being born with a certain name or a certain color of skin has in some illogical way suddenly affected his entire life. It is because of this that the first confrontation is allied to the problem of security and that the reactions to it are those of insecurity.[3] The second confrontation appears some-

---

[3] Chapter 1. The reader will particularly remember the historical development of my concept of insecurity—how I have come to see anxious, panicky states associated with failures in the illogical, unreasonable areas of any origin.

where in the early teens and is characterized by unfairness. The child can now begin to "understand why it might occur"; he begins to see that something (however little) might be done about it. The problem is none the less overwhelming, but it has historical and economic roots that can be described even if not justified. Thus the problem of this second confrontation is allied to that of adequacy, and its overt symptoms are those of inadequacy or inferiority.[4]

Two subsidiary aspects of the first confrontation of Pair 2 cause great disturbance. (a) The child of a minority race may show insecurity due to racial status, even though he has plentiful security in his own family. So the clinician sees the anxiety and panic of insecurity bobbing up in full intensity at times and disappearing at others. (b) Each of these children is very soon faced with the paradox that the parents to whom he must, and does, look for security are the very ones who are responsible for his insecurity from a racial point of view. This ambivalence means that resentment and punishment are wreaked against those whom the child recognizes as his mainstays. The section of this chapter that deals with the chronological development of this problem is pretty meagerly done, as I found it utterly impossible to carry along together the conflicting currents mentioned above. It is especially difficult to give any fair treatment to that part of the first pair of difficulties which might be called the "excuse" part. This is because it seems to be much less socially determined than are the rest of the issues.

Nowadays we seem constantly to be meeting the issue of tolerance. I have not worked long enough in any area to speak with authority on this matter, but I run into a most surprising divergence in the definition of the word. My own view (and I ask no one to follow this) is that one is tolerant of an individual of another race when one sees him as a *person,* entirely eliminating

[4] Chapter 14.

any other consideration. Another, perhaps more frequent, view involves seeing him as a person in spite of his race. In the latter definition tolerance deals only with the adequacy fraction of the problem. I am quite as anxious as anyone to see the disappearance of social and economic discriminations, but if this is done in fairness to one or another minority group we shall only intensify what I have above termed the security aspect of the problem. The sociologist will continue to demand that we be fair to the Negro; the psychiatrist will continue to demand that we be fair to John Doe. And the psychiatrist will argue that every forward move made by fiat for the Negro race intensifies the security issue for each person of that race. To come more specifically to our own material, I am sure that what at first appears to be a change in tolerance is really no more than a shift in the adequacy of the minority group. As long as any line is drawn between certain racial groups, the problems of Pair 1 and the first confrontation of Pair 2 will remain for individual members of a minority race.[5] Only the problems of the second confrontation change markedly as the line of social acceptance moves from that of complete segregation to, say, that of only barring miscegenation. This is not meant to decry the value of a slow progress towards at least removing the issues of adequacy but to face the fact that adequacy is only half the picture.[6] We must always be clear as to how much of change is due to growth in tolerance and how much is due to allowing equal opportunity to various races at different levels of human relationships.

I have been told[7] that persons coming from countries or stocks

[5] The individual's difficulty arises from inability to cope with these problems rather than from their magnitude. Chapter 2 mentions the conflict between the urge to yield to the authority of numbers and the need to feel different from others. Here is a good example of the latter.

[6] For instance, most of the intercultural programs now being fostered in various school systems stress the contributions of various minority races. The psychiatrist feels that even the most frantic efforts at proving that one race is as good as another fail to get at the root of the matter.

[7] By Alvin Johnson for whose insights I have the highest regard.

of small size (no matter how proud or able such groups may be) have much the same problem as those of minority races. This is a statement which would fit into the other things we know about the unhappy world in which we live, but I haven't any data on the subject. That is, my children from Switzerland, Denmark, and other small countries, don't particularly show these symptoms.

I assume that the child is aware of the problem of minority race from his earliest days in that he senses the tensions of the adults about him, but I have very little clinical data here. In fact, the babies of minority race that I have actually known seem to negate the statement just made—if anything, they seem to be less tense, less cranky, and to form fewer bad habits than those of the dominant groups. The only matter worth reporting is the rather frequent statement by older children of minority groups that they do not intend to have children. To judge from this, there must be quite a number of prospective parents who have a real feeling of guilt about imposing their problems on their children. It may be that the tensions of guilt are masked by the workings of many of the other twenty problems of this volume. One moves carefully here, because the results of tensions passed by contagion are extremely difficult to measure even when present.

The problem of minority race first takes shape for the child between three and six. At this time there are at least three significant factors: (1) The unreasonableness of the matter, as stated above. The reader knows my feeling that this is of the utmost importance, that in later life a large part of one's inability to be done with the problem comes from its illogical source. If the acceptance of a person just because he is born in a certain family can give a surefootedness through life,[8] the rejection of a person just because he is born in a certain family reverberates until he

[8] Chapter 1.

dies. (2) The child's weakness—the fact that the problem comes at a time when he feels his inability to meet any sort of serious difficulty. This is frequently stated as a pressing consideration; it has been my feeling that it is not so important as the first. But the matter is not to be treated lightly—if by chance I am wrong, then one of the things we must do is to see to it that, whatever the racial tensions, the problem does not come to the child until he is well grown. My own data here are mostly anecdotal—I have known some adults to whom, I think, the problem of being members of a minority race did not come until they were well grown but in whom the anxiety aspects of insecurity seemed as clearly defined as in persons to whom it came at the usual time.[9] (3) The child's conflict—when he discovers towards the end of this period that his security is dependent upon those who are the source of his insecurity. The reactions of the child belong entirely to the insecurity group.[10] The anxious, panicky symptoms can be seen through life. This is one of the areas in which I have been attempting to get data as to the relationship between adequacy and security. So far as I can discover sizable riches or power do not do away with the basic insecurity involved here, though they may very largely overlay it. One so often sees that no amount of adequacy can provide enough compensations.[11]

This aspect of the problem continues through life in every part of the social structure—school, church, recreation, housing, em-

9 I know of three instances in which children (the youngest fifteen) have been brought up as members of majority groups—to discover their other status when they were young adults. In each instance, however, they knew from the start that they were not living with their own parents, so that the anxiety aspects of the picture that developed may have been dependent on an earlier feeling of rejection by their own families.

10 Chapter 1.

11 It is very natural that the insecure person should seek to meet his needs through those specific material things which give adequacy. Sometimes this is because the person is not clear as to his problem; sometimes it is because he has no other way of trying to solve it. Are not at least some of the much-written-up anal-erotics with their need to amass great fortunes better understood in this simpler though less dramatic picture of the matter?

ployment—there are as many items in the list as there are phases
in our culture. I should be brave enough to give some indication
of trends (or at least where to look for them). But even the least
tolerant reader will excuse a psychiatrist from entering the maze
of the social pressures in this area over the last fifteen years. I
have no hesitancy, however, in reporting that for my patients
every aspect of the problem has been sharpened. The result is
something like that for the deaf person newly equipped with a
hearing device—every sound, good or bad, welcome or unwelcome, comes suddenly booming in with confusing and threatening reverberations.

Somewhere around six minority race status begins to serve the
child as an excuse. Thus all sorts of personal dislikes, affronts,
failures, and so forth can be, and often are, blamed on his being a
member of such and such a race. This is a mechanical aid of in-
estimable value to many individuals—carrying a load of failure
which the individual would not be able to support. There are
many important trends: those in the use and acceptance of certain slogans such as "our criminal record is due to the Italians";[12]
those in the production and popularity of literature which sets
out the unfavorable position of certain races; those in the economic and social disadvantage of minority races.[13] The last give
the child a sort of forewarning of what appears in the following
section. However, the matter affects him differently at different
periods: at first he uses the situation as an excuse for his own failures, then it begins to bear down upon him as a direct cause of
difficulty and frustration.

A special aspect of the problem, which demands statement
here even though it does not directly affect the child, is the social
engineer's use of such shibboleths as "conflict between Old

[12] S. H. Britt, *Social Psychology of Modern Life* (New York, Farrar, 1941), pp.
440 ff.
[13] *Trends,* Chapter XI, particularly pp. 567–583.

World and New World standards" or "interracial reactions" as means of covering more basic interpersonal struggles. Many of us have not been far behind our patients in seeking somewhere afield the sources of sorrow or indecision that lie within ourselves. This appears most frequently perhaps in relationship to the problem of dependence.[14] As one resolves his dependence upon his parents, the distressing personal problems of shame and antagonism are very easily moved over to the less personal area of Old and New World standards. And there are many other examples.

From ten on the child comes in contact with the more understandable factors in the problem—including socio-economic competition. In response to this we see reactions that belong to the field of inadequacy—bullying, overcompensation, and so forth.[15] Here the important trends are those in the sharpness of competition between racial groups. A tragic dilemma lies in the fact that where a minority group is weak and poor, it is protected from much of the hatred and fear of the majority group. As it gains in strength and in its socio-economic footholds, however, the competitive attacks of the majority group become more intense. It is true that if the minority group continues to forge

---

[14] Chapter 16.

[15] I think I can see an extremely important development here. As present statistics are inconclusive, my theory remains largely based on hunch though reinforced by data supplid by D. H. MacNeil, Director of the Division of Community Service for Delinquency Prevention, New Jersey State Department of Institutions and Agencies. My notion is that as there is a decrease in delinquent and criminal behavior among Negroes, there is a parallel increase in neuroses. In other words, as the group attains a somewhat better social status, its reactions to failure in coming to terms with reality begin to resemble those of the Jewish group. There is of course the possibility that there is no actual increase in neuroses but that the better economic position of the Negro permits him to turn to the psychiatrists for help. But the fact that my impression of the change in reaction was formed in the operation of a free clinic points rather to improved social status as the cause. I have discussed this theory at length because of the tremendous importance of the question whether a decrease in crime will merely make way for another equally stubborn and expensive difficulty.

ahead it will eventually be assimilated into the majority group;[16] but until the final stage has been reached, advancement in numbers and power by the minority group only serves to make the task of each of its members the more difficult.

The following observation applies chiefly to adults, and so we have had little actual experience with it at the clinic. It is included here because we see its beginnings in late adolescence and because its results so acutely affect some of the children who come to us. This is the matter of interracial marriages, in which the disparity in adequacy adjustments often greatly strengthens the security tie. So the very fact that disqualifies intimacy from the point of view of social practicability, is the one that ennobles and beautifies the relationship for the two persons involved.[17] For each individual the security tie must be idiomatic—something that is different from any other's relationship (as I have pointed out over and over). This need constitutes a great force towards increasing mixed marriages, which often remain peculiarly successful ventures until social adjustments or the arrival of children suddenly reintroduce the various problems related to adequacy.

[16] The process has occurred in all its phases for certain earlier immigrant waves entering this country.

[17] So often advisers use countless logical arguments against such a relationship in complete blindness to the fact that the very rationality of these arguments is cementing the tie, which has its value for the participants precisely in its unreasonableness.

CHAPTER 14

Adequacy

We see children who have the problem of successfully establishing themselves on the basis of what they are, what they have, what they can accomplish.[1] This is position through intelligence, power, appearance, material possessions, and so forth. It seems a reasonable problem to youngsters in the sense that they feel that they can comprehend the processes involved or in the sense that they can think of themselves as attaining such and such a position. Security, on the other hand, is unreasonable—much of its power lies precisely in the fact that it is independent of strength or intelligence.

An adequate person would be extremely difficult to describe. Indeed, as far as our children go, I doubt that a state of adequacy is ever achieved—perhaps the nearest that anyone comes is to feel at a given moment that he is actually attaining adequacy. Moreover, attainment is largely of a fractional variety. One may be adequate as a checker player, and, in five minutes, be totally inferior as his group turns to basketball. The sort of suffusion which characterizes security[2]—that once established it seems to mellow every aspect of life—is not present here. At the same time, for the child there is a certain satisfaction to be derived from this partial situation in that, in the midst of any number of unsatisfactory relationships, he can bolster himself with "Wait till we come to *checkers*." Very few persons feel adequate in relation to others in more than a very small part of their total adjustment. If we can establish adequacy at one point, we remember that and

1 Plant, pp. 95–105.   2 Chapter 1.

accept our inferiority elsewhere.[3] Here, again, security differs in
that it tinges each part of each day—one would have poor satisfaction in saying *"Tomorrow* I will feel secure."

"Inadequacy" as it is used here is synonymous with "inferiority" as the latter word appears in most psychiatric literature—
with the exception, which I repeat, that most writers in this field
use "inferiority" to cover insecurity as well as inadequacy, describing the insecurity as only a deeper and more stubborn form
of inadequacy. Symptoms delicately shade in actual life, but in
general the reaction to inadequacy is rebellion or overcompensation—and the emotion can be described as fear (to be set off
against the panic of insecurity, with its resultant anxiety). The
clinician sees these things rather clearly in the child's reaction to
an absent father. If the father dies (something which happens to
many children—and which thus seems reasonable to the child),
he has no trouble telling the psychiatrist about it. He may cry, he
may react with various overcompensating bits of behavior as a
result of his loss, but he looks you in the eye as he tells you of it.
On the other hand, if the father deserts the family (which constitutes a threat at the love relationship—at security) the lad tells
about it with panic, averted eyes, and so forth, though from a
material point of view the latter situation may be better than the
other. (The dead father might have left the family penniless, the
separated father may be handsomely supporting the group.)
This illustration may clear the frequent misconception that insecurity is merely an intensification of inadequacy. But it is more
proper to see a qualitative difference and to see that this difference depends on whether the child feels that he can understand
the situation or not. The best explanation of the difference

[3] This is of enormous importance in the school situation, as many resourceful
teachers have long since found. If the child is allowed to feel important in one small
respect or to be a leader in one small field, the whole problem of adequacy is cared
for.

is the child's own breezy grouping of the materials of adequacy and inadequacy under "Why, that's natural."

The therapeutic problems involved in adequacy are relatively simple. A position on the patrol, praise for arithmetic, responsibility for assembling the ashcans—how these have transformed the bully or the noisy attention-getter! The very magic of this is all the more striking as the same tricks fail with the insecure lad. So the unwary teacher or parent in dismay sees some easy trick remake the inadequate, only to fail miserably on the insecure one, who seems to present about the same symptoms. This means that in some situations where the underlying factors are not clear we fall back on the problem of insecurity only as we have tried and failed to deal with them as arising from inadequacy.

The reader is on better speaking terms with inferiority than with inadequacy. Therefore in differentiating a "feeling" from a "complex" it is easier to use the former word. This is a matter about which a great many mistakes have been made—well-meaning ones but none the less devastating. The great popularity which has been accorded to the inferiority complex (gossip masks as dignified when clothed in psychiatric terms!) has hidden, for many, its difference from the feeling of inferiority. In the one case the child feels inferior in a given respect and freely admits it. He hangs his head perchance, but he, the parent, the teacher, and the other children all know that he can't do arithmetic. In the other case he does something about that feeling—he tries to hide it, he shouts his ability in spelling, he bullies weaker individuals, he truants, becomes moody, and what not. This is an inferiority complex. A feeling of inferiority can be treated directly—one talks over the matter of arithmetic with the child and some plan is made. But one can never approach a complex directly. The fact of the complex means that the child is trying to hide his area of inferiority. Therefore in the treatment of a complex we are forced for a period to guess what it is that the child feels inferior about. He must be strengthened in that area, or in some other, before he can afford to dismantle his formidable defenses.[4] If I have spent laborious hours combing my hair to cover the thinning areas, it is depressing to have even my closest friend cheerily remark, "Oh, *I* know why you comb your hair in that way!" An enormous amount of damage is done each day in well-intentioned direct attacks upon complexes. "I know why you are doing that" is a shattering blow to the child who is not particularly interested in what he is doing but is vitally interested in keeping everyone from knowing why he is doing it.

As defined here the problem of adequacy should not appear to the child until somewhere around his second or third year. However, the frame of reference of the problem has been built long before that—and must be sketched. With many the matter of having a child is based largely upon what he can do for the family. The fact that this probably appears to some extent in every such situation does not make it less of a problem where it is the paramount issue. With some frequency a child is planned by one or both of the partners in a marriage as a means of cementing a family tie that has developed more or less serious rifts. Here the results are not to be predicted. It is obvious that a very heavy load has been placed upon the child. If he happens to be a particularly attractive youngster, or if the rift is not too great, the symptoms are less marked. The picture that one gets when the child fails in his mission belongs much more to insecurity[5] than to inadequacy.

[4] A very sizable group will not agree with this—a great number of able and successful adults. They will point out that they have been successful in directly discussing complexes with children. This can be done where the child fully feels that the adult "accepts him for what he is"—which obviously is one of the most satisfying experiences in adequacy.

[5] Chapter 1. But note particularly, page 11, where the distinction is made between the rejected and the unwanted child. What we are discussing here belongs much more to the latter picture.

It is an interesting clinical one, for even though the child comes
to us as a typically panicky soul with the catalogue of evils indica-
tive of rejection, the situation is often cleared up with almost
lightning rapidity. That is, when the child does not "belong"
because he has been looked forward to on an adequacy basis,
some sudden change in fortune may give the answer and thus
leave him free, as it were, to be accepted for himself.[6] Precisely
the same remarks hold for those children who are expected to
make up for an inadequate love relationship with the partner in
marriage. If, for instance, the wife has sought this answer to her
own frustrations, a baby boy may constitute a more adequate
response than a baby girl. But the matter is not so simple as this,
for the father may well be more jealous of a boy, so that there is
the chance that the original difficulties will be thrown even more
into relief. Children also appear as justifications (more especially
for the wife) of each parent's share in the partnership. With growing economic independence for women[7] this factor should lessen
—to increase if the trends are in the opposite direction. This particular aspect of the problem often dogs the child even up into
adulthood, as the parent overanxiously watches every step in continuing to show that "being a parent is a very important job."
Still another prerequisite to adequacy which may be set down
before the child's birth (sometimes very long before) is that he
fulfill certain family plans or traditions. The pressure of such a
need is, in our experience, quite as much determined by each
family group as by the social level or position of that group. That
is, in some well-established families there is a need for a child

[6] Security in one's family (just as in one's religious life) quite frequently comes
by default. It is so much a part of tradition that members of a family deeply care
for one another (or that God cares for each one of us) that the individual often
comfortably assumes that he is receiving or giving security just because there has
been no evidence to the contrary. The more mature reader may remember the disturbance during the 1920's over those poor ritualistic souls who were missing so
much of the adventure of life. The depression and the war have given them other
things to worry about—probably much to their advantage.

[7] *Trends,* Chapter XIV; Young, pp. 564 ff.

to carry on the tradition, and in some "non-established" families there is just as pressing a need for a child who may climb to better fortune.[8]

There is one other factor that plays its part before the birth of the child, though it hasn't the long-standing, deep drives of the ones just mentioned. This is the extent to which the unexpectedness or unwelcomeness of the pregnancy works against either security or adequacy for the child. Lack of money, illness, the crowding upon previous pregnancies all play their part here—and the trend against this would be the increasing knowledge and social acceptance of the control of conception.[9] As I have indicated earlier, I find it useful to make a distinction between the "unwanted" and the "rejected" child,[10] though these terms really run into each other and represent the ends of a continuous series. However, if one were being very accurate, he would say that it isn't the child who is unwanted but something about the child that is unwanted.

It must be obvious that in all the above aspects of the problem of adequacy various social trends are operating to increase or decrease their importance and incidence. Beyond this the task is very much more with the parents than with the child. In many instances they are quite ready to admit that long before the child was conceived they had set up the specifications. The worker must see clearly that if these specifications relate merely to the child's qualities, there is considerable chance that the qualities he possesses will outweigh those he lacks and give adequacy aplenty. However, if these specifications have to do with what the child is to accomplish for the adults or for their marriage, a very heavy load develops—as he is supposed by some sort of miracle to perform a service that might well baffle the ablest of experts.

Before leaving this area I must record that there certainly are

[8] Keeping up with the Joneses sometimes can't hold a candle to keeping up with one's relatives.

[9] *Trends*, pp. 43, 151, 414–423.   [10] Chapter 1.

children who have been looked forward to on the basis of *what* they might give (and thus have never had real security) but who by their sex, cuddliness, and general satisfactoriness so nicely answer the demands for adequacy that the lurking villain of insecurity never once shows its face.

When a birth takes place there is usually a sharpening of every aspect of the problem given in the previous section. Part of this is simply due to the increased drama of birth; part to the actual appearance of the newborn infant, whether healthy, appealing, puny, or crippled. Thus we are interested in trends in obstetrics as to lessened chance of injury at time of birth.[11] At this time also attitudes about "unwanted" children reach an especially critical stage. We often see a miserable and disturbing pregnancy suddenly and completely forgotten in the appealing dependence of the new arrival.[12]

From birth until about five the stage is set and the play is cast for the struggle for adequacy in comparison with one's siblings.[13] Therefore the trends in size of family and in chronological spacing of children are important.[14] In general, where the unsuccessful competition is with younger siblings, the child tends to regress to more infantile modes of behavior; where it is with older siblings, the load[15] is heavy and will result in unpredictable behavior patterns.

In this struggle for a place in the family all the factors previously mentioned in the present chapter play their part, and to

[11] White House Conference, pp. 67–92, summarizes this.

[12] A question that has always bothered me is why one child in a family is rejected when others are not. There are many reasons for this, one of which I see with some frequency—that the mother has not had the care of that child. "I have never felt that he was really my own, he never really needed me and what I could do for him."

[13] Alfred Adler, *The Education of Children* (New York, Greenberg, 1930), Chapter III.

[14] *Trends,* pp. 683–687.   [15] See Chapter 23.

them is added now the growth in the child's physical, intellectual, and emotional characters. At the risk of repetition it should be stressed that this earliest of adequacy struggles keenly presses its claims through life. Such a clinic as our own sees many children who are being pushed beyond their capacity, solely because of the sibling rivalry of their parents.

Somewhere around three—perhaps often before that—the security factors tend to be less obtrusive as the adequacy factors become more and more evident. This is due in part to what we might term the "satisfaction" of the security issues and in part to the fact that the child spends more time in the street and at school. So trends in the growth of nursery schools,[16] and all other developments that make it easier for children to move out from the family group, are important—not only those providing actual facilities but those advising early weaning from the home.

As the first step is taken, one of the new matters that face the child is the social position of his family. Therefore all trends towards the intermingling of groups of different economic and social background are important.[17] In considering this factor the reader must remember the relative importance of the spiritual as compared with the geographical neighborhood. A family may measure its entire development against "neighbors" thousands of miles away. In fact, sharply conflicting standards are often only the difference in the "neighborhoods" of the old and the young in a family.

A second of the new matters that now enter is the whole realm of the child's physical problems. These can be quite practically divided into two groups which considerably overlap. (1) On one hand are those difficulties which actually curtail the child's activities. Here are the bad hearts, the slightly crossed or im-

---

[16] *Trends,* p. 788; White House Conference, pp. 153–166. Of course the war has seen a tremendous increase in nursery schools and probably a large part of that will be kept.

[17] *Trends,* pp. 563 ff.

paired eyes, bad hearing, spinal curvature, and so forth. A child with such difficulties tends to show the restlessness of children who don't have "enough to do." This may express itself in terms of getting unbearably on the family's nerves day after day or of a wide-sweeping, on-the-go, adventuresome delinquent career. Therefore we are interested in all trends towards the amelioration of these conditions.[18] (2) On the other hand is the group of physical difficulties which are not crippling in themselves but which set the child apart from others as being different. Birthmarks or short stature are good examples. There is considerable tendency for these children to hide these matters in blustering fashion. They "draw a red herring across the trail" or noisily announce that such defects do not bother them.[19] Often they seek companions who are younger or of lower social status.

Intelligence[20] begins to play an important rôle in the problem of adequacy when the child is about three, if it is considerably ahead or behind the average of the family or neighborhood. Slight deviations do not show until eight or nine years of age. Therefore all trends in the public's attitude about formal education are important, at least two of which should be named. The first supports the belief that social problems can be solved by more schooling;[21] the second looks forward to school achievement as the badge of social competence.[22]

[18] White House Conference (Section IV, Committee B), *The Handicapped Child* (New York, Century, 1933).

[19] A good example of the differences appears in strabismus. Where the eyes are very slightly crossed they furnish a serious defect, since the child is constantly under effort to fuse the two images. There are many symptoms of physical irritability and fatigue coming from this, though often the defect is completely unnoticed by others. Where the eyes are badly crossed, the child learns to disregard one or the other image, so that his vision is quite unimpaired (though it is true that certain binocular judgments are closed to him). Now, however, he is the butt of every neighborhood joke and must compensate for this difference or inferiority.

[20] Chapter 15.

[21] Educational Policies Commission, *Purposes of Education in American Democracy* (Washington, National Education Association, 1938), p. 10.

[22] *Ibid.*, p. 40. See also New York State Regents' Inquiry, *Education for American Life: A New Program for the State of New York* (New York, McGraw-Hill, 1938), pp. 10–11.

Finally, at this time, there is dawning recognition of certain personality traits that are beginning to crystallize. Such are marked dependence, shyness, instability, stubbornness. The child's reactions are like those mentioned above, except that they are colored by the traits themselves.

By seven or eight years there are new problems in adequacy—rising out of the system of stratification in school placement. These begin at the time when academic subjects first appear seriously, and become more marked as the years go by. Therefore we are interested in trends in school curricula and in school dependence on I.Q. or any other similarly fixed and narrow standard of classification.[23] We are also interested in trends in solidification of school districts or other mechanisms that tend to throw together children from markedly diverse racial or class groups.[24]

The child's response to these later aspects of the problem of adequacy is essentially similar to the one he showed at three or four years of age, but it is colored by two considerations that we tend to forget. (1) As each day passes the child becomes more conscious of what he appears to be to others. This applies much less in problems such as security, where the psychomotor tensions allow the child to be even more aware of his "standing" in the first few weeks or months of life than at any later time. Our pattern of life so frowns upon the messages of the psychomotor tensions, and so exalts verbal or material symbols of expression, that children over three years of age have increasing difficulty in measuring just how secure they are. By the same token, the problem of adequacy becomes more sharpened. (2) Moreover, with the passage of each day, the child's growing strength, intelligence, and

[23] Prescott, p. 247. For example: taking reading out of the kindergarten in many eastern states and putting less emphasis on its mastery in the first grade in some. At this writing there is an interesting reversal in this trend in sections of northern New Jersey.
[24] *Trends*, p. 1019.

integration lend much more persistence and resourcefulness to his side of the struggle. Parents often feel that a child of nine or ten is developing a problem when the clinical picture shows that the child has simply become strong enough to make his rebellion effective.

It is difficult even to estimate the time at which the child begins unloading the problem of adequacy onto material symbols. Money, family fortunes, size of house—all these enter the child's vocabulary by four, but it is certainly not until later that they usefully relieve the child's burden of developing adequacy. Certainly the proximity of neighbors plays a part in the time of appearance and the importance of this mechanism,[25] and there are sharp differences between urban and agricultural patterns. We are interested in shifts in population, since mobility tends to intensify the need for symbols of adequacy.[26] Moreover, the time and depth of development are dependent on certain factors (three easily appear) which concern only the child or his family. (1) Factors of inadequacy within the child (e.g., "I know that I am a second-rater, but at least we have more money than any of our neighbors"). (2) An attitude of this sort soon becomes a dynamic factor in its own right. That is, a child who depends on his family's financial status may soon gain the reputation of being "stuck up," receiving a good deal of social condemnation purely on that score. This increases his feeling of inadequacy, which further presses the need for turning to material sources of bolstering. (3) The matter is further affected, perhaps even controlled, by the extent to which the parents stress the importance of symbols. In some families parents lay store by money, cars, and other material possessions, so that their children do the same. In other families a similar parental attitude leads the children steadfastly to refuse to build any adequacy on such a basis. And there is every shade

[25] Chapter 3, especially pp. 53 f.   [26] *Trends*, pp. 10–17, 167–191.

between, depending on the maturation of any or all of the other problems covered in this book.

This process of impersonalization begins in terms of the family—or one of its members. As early as five or six the child may depend considerably on the size of the father's income, the neighborhood in which the family lives, the size of their house, the make of their automobile, whether they go away for the summer, and so forth. Therefore we are interested in trends in commercial advertising which show that various possessions give social position.[27] Within a few years this very naturally turns more towards what the individual himself possesses—so that the props become what clothes, jewelry, money, and elective positions the child himself has. This state of affairs seems to stem from the child's measure of what is permanent. It is true that in his early years he wholeheartedly prizes his red wagon, or some other toy. However, it is our experience that the emphasis is much more on the possession than on the permanency of the position which is thus given. When a newer or brighter wagon appears the little child will clamor for it—rather than justify or inflate the claims of his own.

It is the popular reaction to inveigh against this whole process of the impersonalization of the problem of adequacy. Many of the more ardent proponents of one or another form of collectivism have been sure that a large share of man's most troublesome problems rests on his striving for the development of adequacy on these impersonal bases. I am not by any means tilting my lance at this windmill in pointing out that the important factor here is not money but the drive for adequacy. Some day it may well be found that money is the least destructive means of measuring adequacy. Certainly in groups such as college faculties or peacetime army camps (where all persons of the same rank have the same material return) one sometimes sees situations develop in

[27] *Trends*, pp. 871–874, 910–911.

which jealousy, bickering, and gossip raise a havoc that makes the financial inequalities of a commercial community seem like heaven. It is a bitter pill for the X's that the Y's have a larger income—but at least the bitterness is in the pill.

By twelve or fourteen, when the above factors are all in full swing, the entire affair is given a new twist, as emphasis develops on personal adequacy when girls and boys become interested in each other. Physical appearance in girls and physical prowess in boys now become very important. We are therefore interested in trends towards the "speeding up" of life—a term used to cover the various social factors operating towards earlier maturity or sophistication.[28] While all the other problems constantly play into the working out of the problem of adequacy, we should perhaps particularly mention here the fact that during early adolescence the child's feeling of strangeness and discomfort combines with intense narcissism[29] to make him particularly vulnerable. In other words, there is a sudden increase in the youngster's inability to face problems evenly. This could be stated in terms of a sharp increase in the permeability or thickness of the envelope or in terms of the youngster's reaction to this—he seems to accept no suggestions, to be open to no material from the outside.

School progress now becomes important in terms of admission to college and choice of vocation.[30] Therefore we are interested in trends in academic requirements and in the whole matter of "going to college" as a badge of social position.[31] The question of earning one's living rather than merely continuing school work also arises. As to this last point, we are interested in trends

[28] I haven't found significant data on this, though so many parents talk about it. One hears that today's children go to parties at about the time we came home, etc.
[29] Chapter 17.   [30] For the trends here see *Trends*, Chapter xv.
[31] Prescott, p. 209. Of course, the war has put all this on probation. It is sixty years since high school and college levels of education have been as free of crystallization as they are today. The reader can count on his fingers those institutions of higher learning which have not printed or mimeographed a postwar readjustment.

in the lengthening of "social" adolescence—that period preceding the person's ability to take some real part in the productive enterprises of the group in which he lives.[32]

[32] *Trends,* pp. 303, 777–779. The high school will do well to remember that there are some things involved here of much more importance than money to the child— e.g., the feeling of responsibility, of being needed, and of contributing something of one's own instead of just giving back (reciting) something that has been offered.

CHAPTER 15

Intelligence

We see children who have the problem of adjusting to the social situation the irregularities and peculiarities of their intellectual development (unusual i.q. and that sort of thing).[1] With some little effort this problem could have been combined with the problem of symbolization.[2] But as intelligence has been given such specialized treatment in the last forty years, as its importance has been so widely advertised, for the present it deserves a chapter in its own right. While this problem is very much affected by the coincident working out of all the others in this book, there is perhaps no other area in which the development of those who surround the child is more important.[3] That is, in general, the rate of growth and optimum development of the intelligence of any individual is established only in relationship to the level of the intelligence of the group in which he finds himself.

The level of this intelligence we assume to be pretty well determined congenitally, for despite the fact that changes can be brought about by environmental adjustments,[4] the i.q. remains surprisingly constant. However, those who are not overawed by its sanctity recognize that it fluctuates and that under certain circumstances the margin of error may be quite large. At the

[1] The psychiatrist hopes to hear less of this notion that problems of human relationship can be solved by knowledge as there is growing realization that Japan had one of the highest literacy rates in the world and that it was what Germany did with her knowledge rather than the knowledge itself which was important.

[2] Chapter 5.

[3] Except for that of minority race status, Chapter 13.

[4] The Iowa studies have by now attained quite a literature. About the best summary of the whole affair is that of Beth L. Wellman, H. M. Skeels, and Marie Skodak, "Review of McNemar's Critical Examination of Iowa Studies," *Psychological Bulletin*, vol. 37, pp. 93–111, February 1940.

clinic it has long been our custom to consider the I.Q.'s of children living under stress as far from final. Such an I.Q. merely measures the child's "effective" intelligence (what he can count on at the moment) and carries no implication as to what his intelligence will be under improved conditions, except that it will probably be higher.

There is no effort in this book at defining intelligence, but at least the following should be said. The present tests for intelligence rest, to a very large extent, on the ability to make generalizations. This is why so many of them involve language and what might be termed "language ability." Criticisms of the latter type of test fail to take into account that one is almost forced to employ symbols for the results of generalization. Language is a system of just such symbols and is therefore the simplest and best measure we have of the ability to generalize. The reader perhaps knows that practically no tests of learning ability exist at present, and he may be one of those who feel that this should be considered a very important part of what we are pleased to call "intelligence." With the further development of this view, there is no reason why language tests should remain the sole means of measuring intelligence. However, as long as the present general view holds as to what intelligence is, they will be retained despite vigorous efforts to substitute non-language scales (none of which has had as yet any wide acceptance except for group testing).

Another matter that needs clarification is the distinction between "formal" and "contentional" intelligence—to adopt Lehmann's terminology.[5] Formal intelligence is what we ordinarily associate with academic ability. Contentional intelligence is often

---

[5] I have been unable to locate the exact citation, but this Danish psychologist should have what tribute I can give to a brilliant bit of understanding. In a personal communication (1942) Professor Helga Lundholm has kindly pointed out McDougall's frequent use of "logical cognitive structure" as opposed to "contentional cognitive structure." Kurt Goldstein (*Human Nature in the Light of Psychopathology*, Cambridge, Harvard University Press, 1940) uses the terms "abstract" and "concrete" to cover something of the same point. This work is peculiarly worth reading. See also the reference to Elton Mayo in note 7.

associated with common sense, shrewdness, "knowing which side
one's bread is buttered on." There is no necessary correlation
between the two in any given individual. We know those who
excel in formal intelligence but who appear as "dumb bunnies"
on every sucker list in the country. On the other hand, every
teacher knows the child who has a low I.Q. but who "has all the
marbles" at the end of the day. She is often quite baffled by the
fact that the leaders, the ones-who-get-things-done, are not always
her most able students. Moreover, while our civilization clings to
the slogan that "knowledge is power," the general public para-
doxically distrusts the practical ability of the scholar.[6] Failure on
the part of psychologists to make clear that the intelligence tests
now in use apply only to formal intelligence has led to a great
deal of confusion among teachers (not to mention parents and
others) because they have not been warned that the I.Q. is a statement concerning only a fraction of what they consider to be intelligence. This is not meant to belittle the value of the I.Q., which
remains a very accurate measurement of something that is extremely important in school progress.[7]

In the discussion that follows the word "intelligence" is used
synonymously with "formal intelligence," except where I have
distinctly noted otherwise. So far there is so little measurable
data on contentional intelligence that despite its great importance we are able to write very little about it.[8]

Because of the part that heredity plays in intelligence, several

[6] Note the very sizable fraction of this concept of impracticability in the term
"brain truster."

[7] The other side of this coin—that there are two sorts of knowledge ("knowledge-
about" and "knowledge-of-acquaintance")—is briefly but clearly dealt with in Elton
Mayo, *Social Problems of an Industrial Civilization* (Harvard University Division
of Research, 1945), pp. 16 ff.

[8] I am sure that it is important enough to be one of the problems of this volume
and have manfully struggled for years to find out what it means to children and
to report some kind of ordered progress in their dealing with it. The reader who is
interested in how little I have succeeded is referred to my "Education for Leadership," in *The Educational Record*, vol. 25, no. 2, pp. 118–126, April 1944.

very important factors in this problem appear before the child's birth. There has been considerable exploration of the effect of heredity on intellectually retarded children but comparatively little of its relation to unusually high I.Q.'s.[9] The significant trends are: those in sterilization[10] or birth control[11] for persons of low intelligence; those dealing with the extent to which the roaming range affects the tendency of this group to marry within its own confines (mingled trends towards increased stratification in opportunity and type of work);[12] and those in the cultural pressures towards eugenics.[13]

At birth the problem of intelligence generally enters only for children who are markedly abnormal (such as idiots). However, two exceptions to this rule should be noted. (1) Sometimes we find parents who are so preoccupied with the future intellectual development of their children, or with proper techniques of rearing, that they overlook the security needs of small babies.[14] There are very interesting trends here—those emphasizing the importance, for life adjustment, of knowledge and high I.Q.[15] (2) We occasionally see rejection situations developing right at birth if some striking trait identifies the child with a member of the family who has markedly low intelligence.[16] The child's reaction to these feelings that he is a second-rater, or is not hungrily wanted in his own right, is a sort of fretful anxiety with which every physician is all too well acquainted and with which he struggles in

[9] See, however, L. M. Terman and others in *Genetic Studies of Genius*, vol. III, *The Promise of Youth* (Stanford University Press, 1930).

[10] White House Conference (Section IV, Committee B), *The Handicapped Child* (New York, Century, 1933), pp. 371–373.

[11] I know of no reliable data here.

[12] *Trends*, Chapter XVI, has many references to this.

[13] *Trends*, pp. 55, 1444.   [14] Chapter 1, particularly p. 12.

[15] *Trends*, p. 342.

[16] "Right from the first day he's even *looked* like So-and-So." It's simple in these situations to say that the rejection probably runs deeper—beginning long before and now activated by the actual appearance of the child. Perhaps that is true—certainly it is true in some cases.

terms of finding a proper feeding formula. But one must not forget that when a child's appearance (in these earliest days) sets him
distinctly apart, it is not infrequent that one or both parents respond with an intensified bestowal of belongingness and protection. Whether this is an intellectual recognition that this child
will need so much more than others, or the result of a feeling of
guilt that they have visited such a handicap upon a helpless person—or both—has nothing to do with the intensity of the "love"
that is given at this time. Such situations constitute a therapeutic
problem of prime importance as the child grows older. So very
frequently advisers of the parents forget how much they need to
suffer in atonement for a markedly defective child. The sound
advice to "put the child away," so that it will not blight an entire
family's life, must often fall on deaf ears.

From the age of six months the child is affected by trends in
increasing the spread of knowledge as to "what progress children
should make."[17] He is now old enough to develop, in response to
parental anxiety, definite nervous habits—in eating, sleeping,
crying, head banging, and so forth. From time immemorial parents have probably looked out with shy fear upon all neighboring children, and neighbors have looked in with supercilious
self-justification upon each baby. There have always been timid
questions as to the progress of one's own, but only recently have
they been given the blessing of authoritative groups.

The issue is much more sharply apparent, as one comes to the
establishment of more complicated social habits at the end of a
year—toilet training, talking, walking, and so forth. There are no
new issues here except the one that will bedevil the therapist for
many of the child's coming years—namely, that for many parents
precisely the things that are most unfavorable for the child's adult

17 To what overwhelming lengths this can go is illustrated in White House Conference, pp. 157–159.

years seem the most favorable in these early months. So many adults get satisfaction from cuddliness, soft dependence, "obedience," willingness to forego adventure—that they look with great favor upon the infant who is actually presenting the least favorable outlook.[18]

By fifteen or eighteen months the child has progressed to the stage where parents are tempted to urge unduly the finer coordinations. Toys involving the hands are pressed upon the child who is ready to use his arms, those involving the fingers upon the one ready to use his hands—these and other similar efforts at hastening the child's activity beyond the rate at which his nerves are ripening[19] lead to keyed-up, tense youngsters whom the clinic will see from fifteen months on. There are rather compelling trends here—in measuring social success in terms of intellectual precocity.[20]

While our experience with actual families includes difficulties with precocity as well as with retardation, our knowledge of the rate of development and its meaning is more complete for the latter. But the effect on the child is apparently the same in either instance, because the problem is not one of absolute development, but rather of development in relation to what the adult world around the child wishes it to be. Nor has this problem been eased by the growing interest which educators have shown in the high I.Q.[21]

The whole matter is very much complicated from around six months on by a factor which, interestingly enough, seems to dis-

[18] This, again, is a confusing aspect in the problem of adoption. Prospective parents find it extremely difficult to realize that what they so much favor at the time of adoption may represent the most distressing sort of problem in later years.
[19] Chapter 6.
[20] Lewis M. Terman and others, *Genetic Studies of Genius*, vol. I, *Mental and Physical Traits of a Thousand Gifted Children* (Stanford University Press, 1925), pp. vii–ix.
[21] Prescott, pp. 233–234.

appear by six or eight years. For this, the highly unscientific but very useful term "jockeying" will do. Like horses at the beginning of a race, children often take a considerable time to "settle into" their final pace. For instance, while we give standardized tests to these young children, we place least reliance on I.Q.'s developed before the child is six.[22] Tests made during these tender years are of great value in determining what stresses on the envelope are arising out of the relation of the environmental demand to the child's ability at the time of study. However, this has little relation to his final pace. As far as the child is concerned the result is an indirect one, in the sense that his nervous tension (shown in the habits of eating, sleeping, or excretion) is produced by the family's feeling that the child's cadence is different from its own—rather than by the cadence itself. We have no evidence that any of these problems of nervous tension come out of rate of intellectual growth—differences in pace seem to be tolerated very well by the child if he is not disappointing to his environment.[23]

In spite of what I am sure is its very great importance, we know practically nothing of this problem during the three-to-six-year period. Certainly this is the time at which the child gets his introduction to the use of symbols. It is amazing to see how much interest the schools have developed in "summer round-ups," in vaccinations and other tests of physical readiness, without ever a whisper as to what the child's introduction to the use of words as expressing experiences has been. I should hazard the guess that many of the stubborn problems of academic learning have their origin in this three-to-six-year period when the child is first learning to develop and manipulate word symbols. It is difficult to

22 Some school systems take the I.Q.'s of all their kindergarten children, but we consider this a questionable practice. It is advisable that these children have tests as to readiness for the first-grade experience (reading), but intelligence quotients that will follow the child through his school years should not be recorded before it is fairly sure that he has settled into his pace.

23 The matters of this section are discussed from a different angle in Chapter 6.

project the progress here since only Piaget has come close to the subject.[24]

There has been some study of the play life of children of this age, and as a result rather pressing trends are apparent in the organization of play life and in the demand for "educational toys."[25] Here again, the child who is slow in developing the same interests as his peers, so that he is thrown back into the home, is often much more satisfying to parents than the more normal child. In these situations of retardation, therefore, the envelope has little tension to handle and we who watch the matter have nothing to worry over except the future.

However, at six the problem suddenly becomes a very acute one, concerning which an enormous amount of study and worry has been expended. Society has dramatized the matter in its expectance that the child be able to start reading in his eightieth month. Here the child's response to failure tends to follow the pattern of inadequacy rather than of security.[26] That is, we see bullying, overcompensating reactions, refusal to go to school, or various childish tricks aimed at punishing the teacher or parent, more often than the anxious, panicky reactions. But, if the child has been previously insecure, it is the latter picture which is intensified. Trends here are of course of enormous significance. There are those in increasing emphasis upon the amount and importance of the reading that must be done in the schools,[27] and those in what might be termed the opposite direction—in the realization that "reading readiness" is a matter that normally is quite variable.[28]

[24] Jean Piaget published three volumes in translation during the late 'twenties. The best place to start is: *The Language and Thought of the Child* (New York, Harcourt, 1926).

[25] J. C. Foster and M. L. Mattson, *Nursery-School Education* (New York, Appleton-Century, 1939), Chapter xiv.

[26] See Chapters 1 and 14.

[27] National Society for the Study of Education, *36th Yearbook,* part I (Bloomington Public School Publishing Co., 1937).

[28] Prescott, pp. 230 ff.

Already the child's success in school is affected by the relative adequacy of his auditory or visual capacities, since the schools tend (with each new fad) to force one or another method of learning on every child. There are interesting trends here in the influence of *Gestalt* psychology on methods of teaching reading.[29] Also there are definite trends in the development of "reading clinics" and remedial reading work.[30]

By seven or eight the same problems appear in the field of arithmetic. We know relatively little about this, partly because we lack knowledge of the intellectual factors involved in arithmetic at this early age[31] and partly because it has been the style up to now to blame poor learning on faulty methods of teaching.

By eight all the areas thus far considered are being actively worked through, with a new set of stresses entering, as the child has been in school long enough to have his own pace of intellectual development thrown into contrast with the one his particular school expects. It will be easiest to divide this into four rather different sets of problems—even if that is frankly an oversimplification of the matter.

There is, first, the problem of children whose I.Q. runs somewhere below seventy-five. As early as eight we find them showing all sorts of rebellions and other inadequacy reactions when they realize that they are failing to meet the rigid classification of society and school. Obviously this is a secondary phenomenon in those instances in which the child is affected more by his own parents' disappointment over the situation than by a direct feeling of failure, so that the matter is often all mixed up with the

[29] National Society for the Study of Education, *op. cit.*, Chapter II, particularly p. 13. Chapter III is also worth while here.   [30] *Ibid.*, Chapter XIII.

[31] A great deal of arithmetic through the fourth grade is a matter of the rote learning of number combinations. Teaching by "flash cards" (carrying combinations for which the children shout the answers) is a favorite method of squeezing the last bit of reasoning out of arithmetic. See Chapter 5, especially pp. 70 ff. and note 16.

issues of security.[32] The trends are mixed here, as one group would meet the issue through the development of special (so-called Binet) classes[33] and the other would keep these children in the regular classes through broadening the base of the curriculum.[34] Also, the trends in the use of a positive as opposed to a negative classification of children for these special classes are mixed—and, again, are of great importance.

Then there is the problem of those with I.Q.'s between 75 and 90. The reactions to failure to keep pace with school requirements are much the same as in the previous group, but the stress and the symptoms tend to develop later. How the school will meet this problem in the next few years is unpredictable. Until the war there was a very rapid development of various vocational types of training, but since the sudden bestowal of legitimacy upon vocational training its proponents have been anxious to rub off the taint of caring for retarded children, who now find themselves quite without a country. Trends in social pressure for academic rather than vocational training are of importance here.[35]

While the more disturbing reactions on the child's part are rather slow to develop, such children can usually be spotted even in the first grade. But even in the higher grades the problem is often not recognized in the case of nice, quiet, polite children— many of whom drift along with regular yearly promotions despite pretty low I.Q.'s. These model youngsters frequently do not have to face the stress inherent in the problem until they change schools or leave school. Thus we have the picture of the acceptable school child ("he's never been the slightest trouble") who suddenly at the start of junior high school begins failing, truant-

[32] Chapter 1.

[33] Statistics of Special Schools and Classes for Exceptional Children. Office of Education, U.S. Department of the Interior, Washington, D.C., 1938.

[34] White House Conference (Section IV, Committee B), *The Handicapped Child* (New York, Century, 1933), pp. 355–357.

[35] *Trends*, p. 342.

ing, or seriously rebelling. The trends of importance are those in the school's recognition of the part that personality traits play,[36] and those in the development of routine intellectual surveys of all school children.[37]

By nine or ten, as the child tries to keep up with children of his age group, a new tension is added to the problem of inadequacy. As the envelope progressively fails to protect him from the knowledge of his difference, he begins to show the same tense, fatigued, nervous pictures that we see in children of any age who are trying to compete with those who are a little older than they. It is worth while to reiterate here that the dull-normal child may be handicapped if he has "good personality traits," as these very often prevent an intellectual difficulty from coming to notice until it has become so serious that the envelope cannot in any way cope with the failure that is involved. Trends in school policy as to promotion on the basis of chronological age, as opposed to school achievement or mental age, are of great importance here.[38]

From twelve on the problem presents no real differences, though it is sharpened by two things. By now the child is definitely having to repeat, or is faced with the more dramatic choice between academic and vocational courses. Also, because he is older, his reaction to the situation is much better organized and much more disturbing from a social point of view—his rebellion in school is more insistent and effective, his truancy more consistent, his compensatory delinquency more pressing. Furthermore, the various unsettlements and drives stemming from his sexual development begin to play their part.[39] Trends in the social acceptance of vocational training[40] are important. Along with them go the trends in the development of vocational schools as distinguished from technical high schools. In addition there

---

[36] Prescott, pp. 214–242.   [37] *Trends*, p. 780.
[38] Prescott, p. 247.   [39] Chapters 9 and 10.
[40] Note the astounding effect of the war upon this.

are extremely interesting trends towards opening the high school to all who have passed through the eighth grade even if it means lowering academic standards.

Then we feel very definitely that there is a special problem involving that unfortunate group with I.Q.'s *just a little below* the average for their community (these might be termed the I.Q.'s between 90 and 95). The difficulty is that the child's ability is not low enough to set him apart, but is low enough to mean that he must be "forever on his toes" to keep up with his group. Here we do not get the reactions of inadequacy so often as the restless, tense pictures of the fatigued child. One sees many disorders in the "higher reflexes"—eating, sleeping, speech troubles, which are all the harder to understand because the youngster is proclaimed "normal" or "able to do the school work." The trends of importance here are those towards what is termed "homogeneous classification"—careful stratification of groups on the basis of similar I.Q.'s.[41] This has many advantages but has never given recognition to the problem of competition for the person who is *almost* as good as the others. Where, however, there is a marked difference—enough for all to recognize—the child has a certain freedom to base competition on other areas of comparison.

In addition, there is an interesting series of problems arising when the I.Q. is well above the average. These have a tendency to appear earlier than problems involving the lower I.Q.'s, as children in this group often attract undue adult interest and companionship at a very early age. There is thus a persistent invitation away from the development of adequate play life with their peers. The vocabulary is usually well ahead of that of the average child.[42] With this often appears a picture of tension (of "nervousness" which may even lead to instability in the higher reflexes of coordination, speech, sphincter control) as the child

---

[41] Prescott, pp. 246–250.

[42] Language factors are at a minimum in the tests used for the age under discussion; they do not assume the major rôle until after the child is seven.

is being held up to the intellectual level of adults. The difficulty here is that his span of attention and "ripening processes" are not ready for this competition—even though his intelligence is. The present discussion, of course, assumes an I.Q. determined without reference to the span of attention. One wonders whether our experience would be the same if there were a widespread acceptance of Kuhlmann's modification of the Binet scales. So many of the difficulties of the present paragraphs are dependent upon small children being thrown with older ones because of an equality in language, curiosity, and auditory memory! There might be quite a reshuffling of these groups of youngsters if the main yardstick were the span of attention.

High I.Q. children also tend to get into competition with children who are somewhat older, and here again one sees the nervous tension that is a part of any picture where the child has to force his span of attention and reach up above his emotional maturity. However, the clearest distinction must be made between children who develop ahead of the average and those who merely have a high I.Q. A three-year-old child who is four in his emotional development, his span of attention, his intellectual development, his physique, and so forth, is a cat of an entirely different hue from the three-year-old child who happens to have an I.Q. of 135. In this and the following paragraphs we are discussing the latter type. What is said in the previous paragraph applies to both types. Trends in the age at which children can be admitted to kindergarten are important here, especially as this event rather dramatically tends to crystallize a relationship that could otherwise remain rather informal and subject to change.[43]

In this country the importance of formal knowledge has been so much stressed that where a child shows a high I.Q. (or, rather,

---

[43] Many communities are not only setting definite ages for kindergarten entrance but are showing an increasing sensitivity to the matter discussed above. That is, regardless of the child's mental age, he must reach a certain chronological age to be admitted.

shows precocity in things which intelligence tests measure) there is every invitation for the family to exploit it—and often to disregard or even discourage other important or appealing aspects of the personality. So a clinic such as ours has experiences from time to time with those insufferable children who are forever showing off their intellectual achievements and who seem doomed to go through life as very successful and very lonely persons. There are significant trends in the cultural emphasis on the importance of formal intelligence and school progress.[44]

High I.Q. children frequently fail to develop any real interest in school, because they are not sufficiently challenged by the curriculum.[45] Sometimes this gives us a child with "not enough to do," restlessly getting into every sort of mischief (often to the extent of serious delinquency). Our most frequent experience is that these youngsters float through school without serious trouble of any sort and without warning anyone that their abilities are not being strengthened and toughened through tasks. Then in college, or at some later time, they break badly over their first real frustration. We have seen quite a number of these brilliant young adults whose histories show no difficulties whatever before the one rather serious affair that brought them to us. The important trends here are those in broadening the school curriculum to make it elastic enough to meet individual variations.[46]

These children with high formal intelligence continue through life to encounter the never ending ripples started by each of the above four aspects of their problem, but in general they find considerable easement of the situation in high school or college or in both. A selective process tends to throw them with stronger competitors, the curriculum tends to be wider and more diversified,

---

[44] *Trends*, p. 342.

[45] One doesn't forget the grotesque. Some years ago a child was referred to us, from about the best of our county school systems, as probably being feeble-minded. He was six and in the first grade—the I.Q. was about 160.

[46] *Trends*, pp. 333–340.

their teachers have been chosen for ability in formal intelligence. There are important trends here in the development of larger high schools (growth of county as opposed to district schools).[47]

It would be easy to assume that children with I.Q.'s which are average for their community have no problems. That is far from being true—of itself mediocrity means an absence of questions and frustrations which lead to growth. This sort of thing is seldom seen by physicians, and when it is, it is hard to put into words. In all fields of medicine we are still trying to get people well instead of trying to keep them well. Thus our ears are not tuned to situations that fail from the start to give striking differences.

The special group of difficulties rising out of questions as to dominance of one or the other side of the body constitute a problem closely related to that of intelligence. They certainly start to affect the child before those discussed in the section just previous, but they come to crisis about the time he enters first grade and are therefore taken up here.[48] Probably there are many more tears over left-handedness in preschool children than a mere clinic would know. Most of our own referrals come during the first three years of school, as the children learn to write. For the years before school attendance, trends in the acceptance of left-handedness as being socially proper are important. How much the child is disturbed by efforts at changing handedness we don't know; I can't remember a single instance of tenseness and restlessness in a child of preschool years in which I felt that this was the only, or even chief, source of pressure.

However, the matter changes sharply with school attendance. I am sure that many, perhaps the majority of children who are

---

[47] *Trends,* p. 1019.
[48] The matter of handedness is placed in this chapter because it has a real bearing on the reading, writing, and spelling problems of quite a number of children. It is a fairly definite entity and could have gone into a number of other places in this book.

changed from left- to right-handedness, accomplish this without the slightest demonstrable difficulty or ill effect. Yet some children certainly develop mirror writing and difficulties in reading and speech from being forced to change.[49] There are two groups of secondary results. One sees "nervousness," restlessness, sleeping difficulties, and bothersome rebellion in children pressed by the task of changing from one hand to the other. And one often sees typical overcompensations in the child who feels different because of the ado that is made over the change—as he frequently has to have special training following the so-called Orton technique.[50] The important trends here are those in the school's attitude as to handedness.[51]

It is surprising how little of this problem of left-handedness we at the clinic see during adolescence. During this period there is such acute self-assay that one would expect a considerable amount of narcissistic worry over any peculiarity. The explanation may be that we work in an area in which both teachers and parents are perhaps especially trained in the matter of the naturalness of left-handedness.

There are many adult problems involved here, but we are not equipped to evaluate their importance. One of these is the widespread notion that left-handed persons are erratic. Then there are various problems of handshaking, being served at table, using implements, and playing games. Interesting trends are indicated here in the making of left-handed tools, golf clubs, and so forth.

---

[49] Perhaps the best résumé of this contested field of the importance of handedness with a good bibliography is Anna Gillingham and B. W. Stillman, *Remedial Work for Reading, Spelling, and Penmanship* (New York, Sackett and Wilhelms, 1936).

[50] See note 49.

[51] In the most general sense the earlier theory was that all children must be forced to write right-handed. Following Samuel T. Orton's work (mid-1920's) the more sophisticated systems left the handedness of the child severely alone. Now a few systems are preferring the right hand in the sense of changing children to that hand if they are not already carrying a heavy "load" (see p. 249) or until symptoms of speech or reading or writing difficulty begin to develop.

It would be interesting to know the effect of handedness on industrial accidents.[52]

As I have already pointed out in the introductory section of this chapter,[53] the problem of intelligence is complicated from the start (but particularly from six on) by confusion of the contentional and formal varieties. Good contentional intelligence is a two-edged sword—its many advantages being often more than outweighed by the fact that it leads to a falsely high expectation in the field of formal intelligence. We see with some frequency nervous and restless reactions in children whose alertness and shrewdness have led adults to demand considerably better school work than they can do. In the school there is growing recognition of contentional intelligence as such and growing acceptance of the large rôle it plays in life adjustments.[54] Plans are slowly being developed to broaden the base of the curriculum so as to give more play to this trait.[55]

This problem reaches into adolescent and adult years in at least four ways. (1) The type as well as the degree of intelligence is considered important in obtaining and holding certain types of jobs. Here there are two exceedingly significant trends: those in demanding evidences of formal intelligence[56] and those in the types of machine that are being used—the trend towards maintenance rather than production workers.[57] (2) It is certainly important in the matter of the availability of friendship ties, as there are trends in the stratification of society on bases that largely de-

---

[52] I suppose that there are such data but haven't seen them.
[53] See above, p. 182.   [54] Prescott, pp. 214–242.
[55] This appears all through Ruth Strang, *Pupil Personnel and Guidance* (New York, Macmillan, 1940).
[56] E.g., attainment of certain grades or diplomas as a prerequisite to employment. Note the effect of the war in reversing such a trend.
[57] J. S. Plant, "The Importance of New Developments in Machine Operations," *American Journal of Psychiatry*, vol. 93, no. 4, pp. 879–884, January 1937.

pend on the I.Q.[58] (3) There is an interesting question as to its importance in the problems of rearing children. So many techniques have been developed in this field and books galore have outlined such a complicated pattern of the child's growth that there is every invitation for parents to feel that formal intelligence of a high order is a prerequisite for the proper rearing of children. While the psychiatrist would scarcely dare to say that it is, rather, a detriment, he has considerable evidence that a high I.Q. is at least a pressing invitation to forget the important emotional components of healthy development. The person of average, or even considerably less, intelligence seems to be freer to develop a warm emotional relationship with the child—and is frequently much more tolerant of the tedious and time-consuming habit-training that is so important in the matter of a right start for the youngster. (4) Finally, there is an interesting matter concerning which rapid changes are occurring. It is not too long ago that the member rôle of the woman made many a young man give wide berth to a girl with "more brains." The trends here towards the acceptance of economic and intellectual equality of the sexes are of great importance[59]—profoundly altering such member rôles.

58 R. S. Lynd, *Knowledge for What* (Princeton University Press, 1939), p. 92.
59 *Trends*, Chapter XIV.

CHAPTER 16

Emotional Development—Dependence

We see children who have the problem of developing emotional maturity. This is not easy to discuss because there is so little agreement as to the standards of measurement to be used. The outline followed in this and the next three chapters certainly has many faults, and it would be difficult to find recognized authorities who agree with its somewhat stark simplicity. But for a number of years I have found it practical and the four problems included—dependence, narcissism, homosexuality, and heterosexuality—are real ones for the individual.[1]

A separation of the emotional and the intellectual developments does not sit easily in these days of psychobiology, psychosomatic medicine, the "whole child." It seems to be agreed that teasing these elements apart should be no more than a laboratory procedure. But there is always the possibility that our patients think of them separately, and it is the synthesizer who is dealing in unrealities! Certainly children and adults both speak of *feeling* this or *thinking* that. The educator thunders that knowledge should be cold. The industrialist grudgingly admits that feelings, like gremlins, run up and down the assembly line. Even grim communiqués speak of matériel and morale. We must watch a bit that we are not too assiduous in making reality unreal.

Various differences exist between the emotional and the intellectual development. There is a certain crispness to the latter which means that the nine-year picture is quite different from the eight-year or the ten-year picture. But the stages of emotional development overlap and color each other (dependence very defi-

---

[1] See also Chapters 17, 18, 19.

nitely strives with narcissism and homosexuality through many
years). Furthermore, in intellectual growth each gain is, to all
intents and purposes, fixed: when the ability to define abstract
words has been developed, there it is—and for good.[2] But no matter how far one has gone in emotional development, he can at a
moment's notice slip back to the most immature levels. Apparently, also, emotional development takes longer to reach maturity, and there is nothing like certainty (which we assume in the
intellectual field) that it has a ceiling year or period.

   The first period in emotional development is that of dependence, so that we see children who have the problem of choosing
between the satisfaction coming from dependence upon some
older and more enveloping or protecting personality or institution, and the satisfactions coming from the feeling that they are
the builders of their own decisions, triumphs, and failures. In recent psychiatric literature there has been so much emphasis upon
the advantages of emotional maturity that we often forget how
many happy and successful persons are quite dependent—emotionally immature. Indeed the latter state of affairs leads to no
personal discomfort or failure unless the individual happens to
be thrown into one or another situation that calls for the exercise
of a mature, or independent, adjustment.
   Up to now there has been little recognition of the fact that
security[3] and dependence are inextricably interwoven during
the early years of childhood. One of the major factors in the
problem of developing independence is this additional difficulty of teasing apart love and dependence. Those of us who
rail at inability to develop independence frequently forget that
many patients have the feeling that in weakening the dependence
relationship they are weakening love ties, which are so important

---

[2] Obviously except for intercurrent illness or accident.
[3] All through here the reader should cross-refer to Chapter 1.

for security. Of this there is every sort of clinical evidence. How frequently the parent of an adolescent says, "He doesn't love me any more," though meaning, "He doesn't depend upon me any more." There is no question that in many families the struggle for independence seriously undermines the love tie. Another way of looking at the whole thing is to recognize the extent in one's own life to which belongingness is expressed through precisely the same enveloping, protecting acts that are insistently invited by dependence.[4] Once more it is difficult to assay, as the years go on, the meaning of these acts and their subtle change as one just as deeply loves or belongs but is no longer dependent.

The war years have given further clinical evidence of this confusion. Social engineers of various sorts have been in a dither about the effect upon the family of the separation of its members —particularly as this increased with the mother's defense work. Dependence has temporal factors—it takes time to help one do something or to teach him to do it for himself. Belongingness has no such time or space limitations. Those who have talked so much during the last twenty years about the relationships of the family will do well to realize that these are expressed by the psychomotor tensions—and that the amount of time the mother spends with the child is less important than what happens while the two are together and the spirit in which the mother leaves. Since women weren't drafted in the war, the critical point to the child was that the mother was away from the home because she wanted to be, not because she had to be. As stated above, we have so long used the habiliments of dependence to fortify the position of security that to a great many families separation in the serv-

---

4 Thus we often improperly use the term "security-giving" in describing a foster parent or teacher of an insecure child. What we mean is "one-who-invites-the-symbols-of-dependence." As used in this book (the reader will remember), security has two aspects: (1) "I am cared for because I am I." This can be fed but rarely satisfied by the cuddling activities that enter this note. (2) "I find a relationship that orients me—tells me who I am." The child can get this only from his own parents or in his religious formulations.

ices and defense work admittedly meant a weakening of belongingness ties, but in no sense was a weakening necessarily involved. It is even possible that experiences of this kind will lead
us to a clearer realization of the absence of temporal and spatial
components in the security relationship. At least they throw
into relief the difference between loving a person and depending
on that person.

It is hard to realize that ten or fifteen years ago dependence
was considered man's worst ill. How many patients were cast
adrift, their cases closed, because they refused to grow up! But
is it a more serious crime to be emotionally dependent than to
have a low I.Q.? Both conditions lead to sorrow and maladjustment unless the environment is fitted to the individual's peculiarities, yet one sees about him many examples of what appear to
be well-adjusted and happy adults who are essentially immature
in regard to the development of independence. How could the
great corporations have become established in this country if
most individuals were not willing and able to forego venture
and hazard for the safe position of being provided for as long as
they did their work and behaved themselves?[5] What would happen to the great interpretive professions if their members suddenly grew up emotionally?

The 1920's were very sure that the matter of emotional development was amenable to external manipulation (and it may
be). Psychoanalysis still pins its faith to the notion that emotional
immaturity comes through the failure to resolve certain complexes and that this failure may be treated through psychological
manipulation. My own view is rather that emotional maturity

---

[5] These are the scalar organizations of Chester I. Barnard. He has not clearly
seen the relationship of emotional maturity to the choice of lateral or scalar pat-
terns in organization but a clear description of these differences is given in "On
Planning for World Government" in *Approaches to World Peace* (Conference on
Science, Philosophy, and Religion in Their Relation to the Democratic Way of
Life, 4th Symposium, New York, 1943), edited by Lyman Bryson and others (New
York, Harper, 1944), pp. 837 ff.

is in some way bound up with certain developments or ripening factors of the autonomic nervous system. In this regard it is notable that a growing number of authorities are tying emotional maturity to the development of the glands of internal secretion[6] which are so closely related to this vegetative system. Without denying the possibility that parents can often strongly influence a child's growth through smothering activities, we can raise the question whether another generation will not find the emotional quotient as congenitally determined as the intelligence quotient. In our clinic experience, for each child who "blossoms out" the moment he is removed from restrictive and imposing adult influences, there are three who cling to their level of dependence regardless of what invitations one makes. This proves nothing, but it opens an exciting vista at the far end of which we see the disappearance of propaganda, as despots enforce the daily consumption of vitamin delta and brave democracy goes on its venture, borne up by the wings of vitamin iota!

In the steps of the problem as outlined below, there are really two processes involved. One is that stated above, the struggle to develop independence (meanwhile teasing dependence apart from belongingness). The other is that of fitting the rate and extent of this development into the rate and extent which the environment demands.[7]

It may be, as one outstanding group of psychoanalysts believe, that the issues of dependence are dramatically faced by each child at birth,[8] and so we are interested in the number and extent of birth injuries and in the ameliorative aspects of obstetrics.[9] At any rate the comfort and protection received during the next few

[6] A summary of this appears in Prescott, pp. 49–53.

[7] Chapter 6—the problem of cadence or rhythm.

[8] At least an outstanding school among the psychoanalysts has been able to construct a whole system of dynamisms about this (see Otto Rank, *Trauma of Birth,* New York, Harcourt, 1929).

[9] Summarized in White House Conference, pp. 67–92.

weeks serve as an invitation to dependence throughout life. As soon as the child faces his own weakness and inability to control the environment he begins to recognize how much satisfaction he gets from his parents. It is at this time that the tie between belongingness and security is made. This is such an important part of the whole problem of dependence that it is possible to measure all the later experiences in life in terms of a dependency relationship with parents or parent substitutes—the school, the Church, the State, the employer, the friend, the physician, the husband or wife.[10] Trends in early family relationships[11] and trends in housing and other socio-economic conditions that strengthen dependence on the home have bearing here.

Throughout infancy the child receives numerous solicitous attentions from parents. By six months he definitely begins to sense that discomfort and illness are better cared for by others than by himself. Trends in adult education in regard to the care of infants[12] and in the employment of mothers[13] are important here; and so are trends in medical, nursing, and hospital services.[14] In the latter connection it is interesting to note that doctors and dentists have begun to realize that it is important for them to represent pleasant experiences to the child.

At two or so the child begins to form a new set of impressions about his physical weaknesses. As he is placed in situations of less supervised play with neighboring children, he may come in contact with a "destructive competition" that is quite different from the "protective competition" that his parents show him.[15] If he feels the need to carry over the latter into his play life, he may seek companions who are enough older (say three years or more)

---

[10] See p. 209.　　　　　　　　　　[11] *Trends,* Chapter XIII; pp. 714–716.
[12] *Trends,* pp. 792 ff.　　　　　　[13] *Trends,* Chapter XIV.
[14] White House Conference, pp. 93–112, summarizes this. Editor's note: The reader is also referred to the report of the American Academy of Pediatrics, *Child Health Services and Pediatric Education,* New York, Commonwealth Fund, 1949.
[15] Plant, pp. 258–259. The parents play upon and strengthen those things the child can do; his peers are more interested in exploiting the things he cannot do.

to continue the parental type of competition. The age, the strength of his companions all play a part. When these new pressures are too great (i.e., when the envelope does not succeed in keeping out their crude import), we see the child reverting to earlier and more dependent behavior (complaints of illness, bed wetting, baby talk, refusal to play, etc.). At this same age the child's dependence is reinforced by the authority of age, possession, and love.[16] Trends in nursery school development[17] and trends in adult education that stress the early independence of the child[18] are important.

By four the child begins to show real satisfaction in his own accomplishments. Sometimes he expresses this in terms of pleasing those he is dependent on. We assume that this is the result of identification ("I like my parent; I like what my parent does; I'll think well of myself if I act as my parent does"). But as the process of identification begins to place the child in competition with, rather than dependence upon, the parent we often see forms of behavior that are meant to disturb adults. In our clinic experience it is about this time that children overcome their own sense of weakness by developing leadership in one or another matter in which they can succeed. As the child begins to grow away from dependence[19] he seems to get satisfaction from trying out his own powers of action. A great deal of his destructiveness, of his asking endless questions, and of his sticking his nose into everything comes from the positive feeling of satisfaction in the integration of new reflexes and the attainment of his own ends.

All the issues of this section are again fought through at five as the child enters school. At this time the satisfaction that he finds in the dependency relationship is increased or decreased as

[16] Chapter 2.
[17] White House Conference, pp. 154–156; *Trends,* p. 788.
[18] *Trends,* pp. 792–794.
[19] Some authorities therefore define adolescence as beginning at this time.

the envelope allows him to see his parents' traits reflected in the
teacher. When the school environment imposes more demands
or exerts more pressures than the child's feelings of independence
(or drive for independence) allow him to accept, regressive types
of behavior appear. There are extremely interesting trends here
—those in the age at which children enter school;[20] those in the
age at which academic work is expected;[21] those in the school's
recognition of the identification between parents and teacher;
and those in the school's recognition that the classroom is not
only a place where children learn certain rote material but also
a place where they live together.[22]

In early adolescence the issues discussed are thrown into sharp
relief by two new developments. (1) A marked increase suddenly
takes place in the child's vulnerability, with rapid and wide
swings from noisy independence to contrite dependence—and
back again. (2) Actual physical separation from the family emphasizes the problem of separating love for one's parents from
dependence upon them. We see individuals who identify the
two issues throughout life—either remaining completely dependent for fear of shattering the love tie or rejecting every shred of
affection for fear of remaining dependent. We see others who
from an early age clearly distinguish between the two issues.
And we see every shade between these two extremes.

During the early teens the old crosscurrents continue, and two
new ones appear. Dependence can now be transferred from persons in the child's immediate orbit to ideals and future goals;
and with the increased danger involved in working out the
sexual adjustment, there is every invitation to parents to reaffirm
their power of control.[23] Therefore all trends that lessen the social implications of sexual intercourse (e.g., knowledge of con-

[20] White House Conference, pp. 153 ff.   [21] *Trends*, pp. 782–784.
[22] Prescott, pp. 193 ff.   [23] Chapter 7.

traception and economic independence of women)[24] are important.

To recapitulate. In infancy the child recognizes these same dependency values in persons other than his parents. This first appears for aunts, grandparents, or others who live with the family or are closely tied into it. The issues seem to work through as they do for parents—whether these members of the "outer family" supplement the parents or take the place of parents when the latter don't possess traits that easily lead to dependency on the child's part. Trends in the disappearance of the clan family[25] are important.

It sometimes happens that neighbors play a similar part in working out the problem—the child finding through chance acquaintance persons who are either so closely identified with his parents that they can maintain a relationship that has proved satisfactory or so different that they offer a dependency that the child had found it difficult to develop towards his own parents. Something of the same thing holds for teachers as for neighbors. The teacher is in a position of authority somewhat similar to that of the parent, which particularly invites dependence on her. But since she usually ceases to be part of the picture during the child's vacations and after he goes on to the next grade, she holds his dependency much less on the basis of being a person in a certain position (like the parent) than on the basis of having certain traits or "answers to problems" which are acute at the moment. Trends in the school towards recognizing the importance of these issues are, of course, of major importance.[26]

As the child finds that other persons or groups can reinforce or take the place of his parents in the dependency relationship, he comes upon the Church—though my data gives no age for this.

[24] *Trends,* Chapter xiv, and p. 151. [25] See Chapter i, note 26.
[26] This appears all through Prescott, pp. 193 ff.

The earliest feeling seems to be "I am supposed to go," and this easily appears by four. Then there appears, at varying ages, "It is interesting—or beautiful." Certainly by adolescence the child can feel that "God will take care of everything," but I do not know exactly when and how this last starts.

The various parental substitutes envisaged in this section are important in all cultural patterns, but they seem particularly so in our own because the disappearance of the clan family has put such a tremendous load upon the parents. This loading of the emotional problems upon the shoulders of two persons sharply increases the hazards in the process. When they, for any of a legion of reasons, fail to provide anything at all approximating the child's needs as he works out his problems, he must hunt these answers along devious paths or in faraway places.

Children also transfer dependency to material objects. Our data seem to indicate that this is a universal phenomenon but that the *extent* to which it is done is somewhat dependent upon the answer to the satisfaction which the child has gotten from the persons discussed in the previous sections of this chapter. The chronological development and the social trends are about the same as for status preservation.[27] Indeed the two problems are often so closely interwoven that it is difficult to tell how much of the child's relationship to money, goods, possessions, and so forth, is fear that their absence will destroy status and how much is comfort in the various satisfactions they bring.

By adolescence the dependency problem has frequently worked its way over into the matter of choice in work or pro-

[27] Chapter 3. But particularly note trends in population concentration, as this certainly puts a premium on the use of material symbols as expressing human goals and attainments (*Trends,* pp. 445–446); also trends in advertising which assure the reader that place and position are given by possession of certain objects (*Trends,* pp. 871 ff.).

fession. The child recognizes that certain occupations are adventuresome, full of challenge to individual initiative and freedom, while others are interpretive or "protected." Trends in the number of persons engaged in various occupations are of importance here, but the matter runs deeper. Two examples will suffice. The first is the trend towards the disappearance of "small business," with its challenge to the courage and individuality of each owner. Another is the interesting trend towards entirely new fields in the interpretive professions (e.g., the development of so-called "administrative law"). This whole area is somewhat foreign territory to us, as we see few patients who are over sixteen. It is true that most of our patients know what they are going to do "when they grow up." But up to sixteen this is largely based upon identification, even though the child frequently does not consciously recognize it as such.

While it cannot enter our discussion here, the struggle goes on in fascinating fashion through life. Choice in marriage (and living through this relationship), attitudes towards employers, possibly many of the problems of class struggle—all illustrate the kind of thing that is certainly deeply affected by the need of each individual from time to time to depend upon persons or things or to throw off that dependence.

CHAPTER 17

Emotional Development—Narcissism

We see children who have the problem of adjusting to an intense interest in themselves—an overpowering egocentricity. In my formulation it is the second stage in emotional development—as stated in the previous chapter.[1] This does not appear as a major issue until the child is ten or eleven, and during late adolescence it usually ceases to be a compelling problem. However, in certain emotionally immature persons it remains dominant throughout life—and it is a smaller component (or problem) in the adult lives of all of us. Just as we never shake off dependence, so we are never rid of the preoccupation with what we are, what we think or do.

Because the term "narcissism" has had wide currency—very largely on the basis of the formulations of the psychoanalytic school—it is necessary to explain the relationship between my own definition and this more popular conception. Psychoanalytic literature constantly refers to a "primary"[2] as opposed to a "secondary"[3] narcissism. Primary narcissism is assumed to exist in infancy, as the baby thinks of the whole world as continuous with himself, and it is intensified through the natural withdrawal of outside repositories for emotional expression—the phenomenon of cathexis. What is "I" at birth is rapidly reduced by independent action of various parts of the environment, but its emotional load is, by so much, intensified. Thus the mechanism of primary narcissism is an essentially negative one. In both the psychoanalytic view and my own the narcissism of adolescence

[1] See also Chapters 18 and 19.　　　　[2] Healy, pp. 102 f.
[3] Healy, p. 10.

is a "positive" mechanism. Here the child "willfully" turns his attention to himself, contemplating his image with the same absorption that obtained for Narcissus himself. The reader will find that my view of the dynamism involved in the earlier process differs markedly from that of the psychoanalysts,[4] but that is perhaps of little importance. The important matter is that what I term narcissism in this book is familiar to most readers as "secondary narcissism."[5]

This almost morbid interest in each small detail in one's life does not suddenly appear with the onset of adolescent changes; wisps of it drift across the child's life as early as four or five, but without presenting enough of a problem to raise any serious tensions or tasks for the envelope. It comes into its own as the second stage of emotional development, gradually nudging out dependence, as it will be later replaced by homosexuality. The reader will remember that the emotions of each individual move back and forth on this scale of development but at any given time are never more than preponderantly in any one area. Whether one chooses to assume (as I do) that the phases of emotional maturity advance and recede or (more popularly) that dependence, narcissism, homosexuality, and heterosexuality are constant components of the personality always vying for ascendancy, seems a matter of wording.

To those interested in the happiness of children it seems unfortunate that this period of intensified self-examination should coincide with the very dramatic physical changes in both the boy and the girl. These physical changes act as crystallizing points for acute self-appraisal. Each primary or secondary sex character is combed over for possible differences from the typical. The possi-

[4] J. S. Plant, "Negativism: Its Treatment and Its Implications," *American Journal of Diseases of Children,* vol. 61, no. 2, pp. 358–368, February 1941.

[5] It has seemed to me most unfortunate that the same word has come to be used for two such different *processes*—though I should be the first to admit that in both periods the individual is very largely preoccupied with his own mental life.

bility that narcissism may be awakened by precisely these changes doesn't soften the issues involved here. Obviously through all of this the problems of the feeling of difference and the sense of guilt are of the greatest importance.[6]

Less has been written concerning those who remain at this stage of emotional development than about those who remain dependent[7] or homosexual.[8] The issues seem to me to be the same as those discussed under dependence. We shall save much wear and tear when it is generally realized that environmental demands must be adjusted to those who are emotionally immature—as they now are to the intellectually immature. This view admits that many who appear to be emotionally immature are not really so (just as many who appear to be mentally defective are, in actuality, merely not living up to their real intellectual capabilities).

At about eleven the child begins to develop an intense interest in his own traits, growth, and goals. Without any claim that trends in modern advertising (e.g., those in the general field of cosmetics and aids to popularity) have been the source of this, there can be no denial that the adolescent could not worry any more about minute details of get-up more than does the advertiser. It would be interesting to know how much of the child's narcissism is impelled by his sense of vulnerability during a period of fundamental internal readjustments. Certainly the earliest stage to appear is one of preoccupation with physical development or appearance. Freckles, the curl of the hair, body size—these and countless other matters of similar sort are questioned, reviewed, criticized—partly in anxious dismay, partly in panicky search for

[6] Chapter 4. And all the complexity of intertwining drives mentioned there are present here. Differences in the development of the secondary sex characters invite an intense feeling of individuality just as they become involved in an area upon which society has bestowed a tremendous load of guilt.
[7] Chapter 16.   [8] Chapter 18.

parental assurance. This is particularly true of the secondary sex characters, size or development of genitalia, body hair, fat deposits, voice, and so forth.

It is our feeling that the sexual problems of narcissism should be separated from those of the preceding and following periods. Up to this time, masturbation and other perversions have been largely driven by the need to show that one is growing up;[9] they now involve curiosity as to "how it works" and worry over "whether it works as well for me as for others." Unlike the physical satisfactions of the stage that follows, which are intense and local,[10] those of narcissism are diffused over the whole body and are often mixed with pain. The reader will remember from the earlier discussions of sex[11] that our data relate almost entirely to boys, as we know very little about the ways in which girls express their sexual interests.

There is an interesting trend here that is not easy to explain. It is not clear why society has developed a more tolerant attitude towards masturbation though maintaining rigid taboos against exhibitionism, sodomy, and mutual masturbation, especially as the latter phenomena nearly always have the same motivating force as masturbation during the narcissistic period.[12] It is true that there are all sorts of personal interdictions against masturbation, but officially (i.e., in the courts) we have no interest in sexual phenomena unless they involve other people. Thus society ignores masturbation but majestically forces exhibitionism (which is an expression of the same normal drive) into hidden ways. The psychiatrist tends to take the opposite view, for sexual behavior that is closeted, carried on in secret fear and guilt, is extremely difficult to deal with.

[9] Chapter 10, pp. 134 ff.   [10] Chapter 18.
[11] Chapters 9 and 10.
[12] I.e., to experiment with and try out the new mechanisms. The use of these perversions as substitutes for the tabooed heterosexual acts does not usually appear before the homosexual period (Chapter 18).

Why children react to their own differences with feelings of inferiority is an interesting but baffling question.[13] It is true that they have only recently left a long period of weakness and dependence, and that the many changes of adolescence lead to a vulnerability during that period, of which they are aware. These may be the only elements involved, but the fact that the child's reactions tend to be those of overcompensation rather than of panic or anxiety suggests other possibilities.[14] One of the more distressing and stubborn of these reactions is attraction to "those of lower social status," where obviously his fancied blemish is compensated for by his position. Less troublesome, but equally stubborn, are all those loud expressions of voice, clothes, or manners which draw a red herring across the trail of his certainty of inferiority.

At the start of the narcissistic period the child will often follow about and copy an older member of the family or some other adult with whom he feels he has a certain trait in common. While this gives the superficial picture of identification,[15] and the end results are much the same, the mechanisms are different. In the imitation of the narcissistic stage the affinity is based on a single trait, whereas in identification it is based on the total personality of the older person ("I like to be like him").

By fourteen or fifteen the child begins to show the same interested appraisal of his ideas that he earlier did of his physical traits. Out of this frequently develops a disputatious drive because he cannot afford to have his ideas agree with those generally current. He feels it necessary to prove that he "sees things much more clearly" than has any previous generation. Part of this arises from the close interweaving of the problem of difference[16] and

[13] Chapter 4.
[14] Both patterns appear, but one *much more* than the other.
[15] Chapter 16.   [16] Chapter 21.

part from the matter mentioned above—the child's deep feeling of uncertainty and weakness about his views—a feeling which he covers with this noisy show.

Analogies are dangerous only if they designate rather than illustrate. With this stricture I find it useful to think of this age as the time when the child becomes a translator. He now begins to realize that it is up to him to make all the past into something that is his own—that can be handed on to the future. So we adults are often confounded by endless arguments, when the child is saying only what we say—but in his own terms. We are equally confounded by his need to feel that he is not agreeing with us, and often we give advice, blind to the fact that the child is unable to follow it just because we give it. As a shorthand way of speaking, I find it convenient to push the analogy further by distinguishing among those who "prefer it in the original" and those who are literal or free translators. And then in each generation there is a handful of those who can catch the majesty and meaning of the past and add to this in some small way the spirit of their own lives and time. Such an analogy demands acceptance of the psychiatrist's basic hypothesis—that the individual translates culture. The sociologist disagrees with this, maintaining that the individual transmits culture.[17]

Egocentricity is fertile soil for paranoia, so that one is not surprised at the marked paranoid swings that appear all through the narcissistic period—reducing everything that is said or done to terms relative to the self. One sees an increase in "touchiness" and in all those phrases that connote suspicious sensitivity ("I know you really mean me when you talk that way"). Some individuals never grow beyond this—in a few instances eventually developing a true paranoid psychosis.[18] With most, the matter

17 This depends upon the extent to which one feels that the envelope plays its part in the whole affair (see Introduction and Chapter 23).

18 However, note the exciting views expressed by Norman Cameron in "The Development of Paranoic Thinking," *Psychological Review*, vol. 50, no. 2, pp. 219–

subsides into a small component which remains throughout life but never organizes into anything encompassing the whole personality.

An important aspect of the problem of narcissism is that of the rapid growth of interest in the mystical, in "causes" that transcend the child's control. It is at this stage that adolescents are most easily recruited to movements in which they "can find themselves by losing themselves." How much of this interest in and giving oneself up to the mystical is a loyalty in our usual sense of the word and how much is an identification by the child with the power and drive of this "greater cause,"[19] I don't know. Nor, probably, does the child. As the youngster dedicates his life to this or that, it is very possible that the envelope is functioning in relation to the problems of both dependence and narcissism.

These two major interests involved in the problem of intense self-interest run their way up into adult years—as is the case with all the other problems discussed in this book. Two adult pictures appear—and of course in every conceivable combination. None of us completely throws aside or outgrows this narcissistic trend. Its interest in self-assay and its compelling drive that each become engulfed in some greater cause are threads that are never lost.

Many individuals get hung in the narcissistic stage of emotional development just as many others never grow beyond the period of dependence. These individuals make excellent adjust-

233, March 1943. The author's conception of paranoia as a problem in communication describes another facet of this disease. It is perhaps fair to say that the fundamental problem of poor communication with the outside world is intensified by (or given fertile soil in) the narcissistic trends we all have.

[19] This is of left-handed importance—since much joining of the Church is obviously determined by social fiat (the rites of growing up). I have included the point here partly because we know some children who join the Church at this time without noticeable parental or Church pressure and partly because the high incidence of joining the Church at the climacteric indicates that the sexual stresses have some relation to the phenomenon.

ments if their needs are understood. (Certainly many of the great political leaders have been of this type—impatient of anything but praise, strong through the cause with which they have identified themselves.) When their needs are not understood, their lot is a dreary one—searching in unending fashion for adulation and interest in a world absorbed in its own affairs.

No chapter in this book has fewer references to compelling social trends. Perhaps this is the best proof one could adduce as to the intensely personal nature of narcissism. Many commercial organizations, and not a few political leaders, have made use of its drives, but I know of no one who has even dreamed that he could bend or blunt its purpose and interest. Even if there were no other reason, this positive, willful, not-to-be-denied characteristic would set the phenomenon apart from what is so frequently called "primary narcissism."

CHAPTER 18

Emotional Development—Homosexuality

We see children who form deep attachments for others of the same sex (or for much older persons of the same or even the opposite sex[1]) during late adolescence. I term this the "period of homosexuality," and I consider it a normal part of emotional development.[2] It is characterized by "crushes" and intense hero worship. Whether one thinks of the period as the third stage in emotional development or takes the more common view that it represents the overt appearance of the homosexual component which is in each one of us, is a matter of choice. In either case the main consideration is that for some three or four years the homosexual drive is predominant—its problems trailing on through adult life.

The use of "homosexual" in this book is therefore not to be confused with the popular use of the term (to connote a perverted expression of the sexual drive).[3] But to some extent the two uses of the term overlap, as it is true that unusual happiness in the homosexual stage of emotional development or a delay in entering the heterosexual stage may be dependent upon precisely those physical factors which are so prominent in the more usually accepted concept of "homosexuality" (effeminacy in men, masculinity in women).

Many of the phenomena of this period are far more disturbing

[1] See below, p. 221.
[2] Following dependence (Chapter 16) and narcissism (Chapter 17). Our clinic patients (for the most part not over sixteen years old) give us a less complete picture of this stage than of any other except the fourth stage, heterosexuality (Chapter 19).
[3] Healy, pp. 103, 400.

to the adult onlookers than to the child—who has some not-too-clear realization that they don't count, that the responsibility involved is not the same as in heterosexual adjustments. Thus the child is free to experiment in developing emotional ties just because they are not lasting. The objection may be made that the child has no realization of this—that at the time, he thinks of the tie as permanently satisfying. This is true in some cases. It would be against the facts to say that all children are really held by the pressure of a cultural pattern that demands the union of contemporaries of the opposite sex. But it would also be against the facts to deny that most children carry through their homosexual activities and interests on the firm foundation of a biologically and sociologically determined drive to heterosexuality. Also there is the factor of "safety" (there can be much sexual satisfaction in the physical sense without danger of resulting pregnancy). I find the latter rarely verbalized by adolescents, but it is given as a consideration quite frequently by more mature and habituated homosexuals. The same may be said for the common feeling that there is less danger of disease.

Sometimes adolescents seem to experience the deep and rich feeling of beauty and steadfastness which arises in many of the adult homosexual situations precisely out of the cultural taboo —the fact that the relationship means all the more to the persons involved because it is one "that shouldn't exist." To what extent this helps to work out the problem of security[4] and to what extent it represents a limit in emotional development, it is difficult to determine. There is this to be said, however—that all the adolescents whom I have known to be involved in deep and lasting homosexual adjustments were persons who made very poor social adjustments.

A certain number do get hung at this stage of development as indicated earlier.[5] It is difficult to discover how much of this is

[4] Chapter 1.   [5] See particularly Chapter 16.

dependent upon environmental as opposed to individual influences. I have felt that if the environmental factors were the dominant ones, the largest fraction of such emotional retardation would express itself at the homosexual stage. However, narcissism seems to be quite as common as homosexuality in adult years, and dependence is far more common than either of the other two.

The most prominent trait of the period of homosexuality is the formation of strong attachments to others of the same sex, and about midway in the years of adolescence. We are so accustomed to these so-called crushes among girls, that we sometimes overlook the fact that they also occur among boys. While there is the strongest social taboo as to genital contacts, it is perfectly normal for children to derive great satisfaction during this period from every sort of bodily contact with others of the same sex. This seems to be free from the tentativeness and fear that accompany the same contacts with persons of the opposite sex. Trends in co-education and in recreational developments (in so far as they stress the separation or mingling of the sexes in play or competition) are of importance here. This whole matter particularly expresses itself in the development of fraternities, sororities, and other closely knit groups involving the same sex.[6] Obviously it extends up into the adult field, where we see many who are still primarily interested in these groups and their complicated rituals.

The period of late adolescence is the last "normal" one for the

[6] It would be interesting if we knew its relationship to the predatory or defensive gangs of this period. F. M. Thrasher (*The Gang*, University of Chicago Press, 1927) has collected an enormous amount of data on the subject, but he doesn't give help on this point. Some group workers (e.g., Professor Grace Coyle) have looked upon these close associations as an effort to build a bridge between the security of childhood and that of married life. I prefer to use the term for a more specific phenomenon, though many of these ties present the "symptoms" of the security relationship.

development of strong attachments to persons of the same sex. Therefore we are interested in trends in the age of marriage[7]— taking this as the best measure (though not too good, at that) of the time at which it is easy and comfortable for persons to enter the heterosexual stage of development. The point here, as in so many places in this book, is that quite regardless of what theory the psychiatrist may wish to spin (and what therapy he may wish to apply) as to homosexuality, the age at which marriage is sanctioned has an important bearing.

Less common, but still characteristic of this period, are extremely strong attachments with older persons of the same sex. These are not to be mistaken for the very common identifications with older persons. In the crush there is great satisfaction for the child in physical contact—and not so much interest in copying some trait of the older person as in winning his or her favor.

Very often children at the homosexual stage of development also form crushes on much older persons of the opposite sex. While these may appear in various situations, we most frequently see them in the pupil-teacher relationships. On occasion these attachments go on through to marriage, and in such cases (quite regardless of what they mean in terms of happiness to the persons involved) they are invariably the source of much unsavory publicity.

The second outstanding characteristic of this period is its development of intense hero worship. It's possible to see this as an extension of the mechanism of the previous section, though the child doesn't see it as such and as a practical matter it does not have the same affectional values. In this homosexual period the child's "emotional interest" is once more directed outward, as in

[7] *Trends*, p. 680. The gradual but insistent rise in the age of marriage had a sharp acceleration during the early years of the depression but had begun to turn in the opposite direction by 1939 and rapidly lowered during the war. One sees no reason why it should not slowly and definitely rise again.

dependence (instead of inward, as in narcissism) but is not yet truly heterosexual. It may therefore rest upon any person who is not a heterosexual "liability," and in this sense both the hero and the object of a crush can be thought of as answering the child's need.

The trends that seem important here are those in crowding[8] and those in education and literature towards the "debunking" of heroes. In the reference just made I have given some evidence that crowding seriously affects the mechanism of hero worship—not only in making it more difficult for the child to develop hero images, but also in forcing him to depersonalize heroes—measuring them in terms of their accomplishments rather than of their personalities. There is, of course, a great deal of identification with the hero. This works in one of two ways—either beginning as an identification with a person, so that the child assumes many of the hero's traits, or starting at the level of a trait ("I am short, Napoleon was short"), and spreading from that to identification with the total hero image. This is full of hazards for the individual through the rest of life, since the major stuff of any hero is a projection mechanism (the hero is always what I think him to be, or what I want him to be) and is therefore constantly threatened with dissolution through his actual performance. The constant danger that the "truth will out" is thus of serious importance to the individual. The sudden discovery that, even in some quite minor matter, the object of worship does not fit the image that has been built often leads to profound dismay and depression, which is difficult to understand until we recognize that it is the individual's own aims and purposes that have been destroyed or put on probation.

[8] Plant, pp. 216–217. As this reference deals with the phenomenon of hero worship in a crowded industrial area, the increasing number of such areas (or the decentralization involved in much of modern city planning) is important.

CHAPTER 19

Emotional Development—Heterosexuality

We see children who develop in adolescence an interest in persons of the opposite sex of approximately the same age. This interest is on an equality basis that looks forward to a mutual sharing in some such adventure as marriage. The development and adjustments of the problem are undoubtedly closely connected with (or maybe the same as) what we term "emotional maturity." Anyone acquainted with psychiatric literature is certainly aware that emotional maturity has never been adequately defined. Emotional immaturity at various levels has been fairly well described, but for the most part maturity has been defined negatively by noting the absence of the various phases of immaturity. The psychoanalytic group stresses the development of the true heterosexual drive at a much earlier age than I do. In fact, psychoanalysts recognize the appearance of the sex drive in infancy—splitting it into its homosexual and heterosexual components. I should agree that small children have heterosexual interests in other children as well as in adults (for instance, in marriage with the mother on the mother-child basis), but I maintain that drives for possession far outweigh drives for sacrifice—the sexual interest is in preservation of the *status quo* rather than in venture.

Three matters serve particularly to disturb teachers and parents (and their vicars) during this hectic period of the teens. (1) The sexual urge comes strongly at this time, but it is not balanced with maturity of judgment. (2) The adolescent frequently seems to be "rehearsing his part." Though not verbalized, the implication that "this doesn't count" unquestionably figures in much that he does. Sometimes this experimentation takes the form of overexpressive attraction to an older person of the opposite sex. The picture is not clear because it includes certain carry-overs from the homosexual stage.[1] (3) The very rapid spread of the knowledge of contraceptives[2] and the apparent narrowing of the importance of marriage (removal of functions from the family and increasing economic independence of women) have robbed sexual intercourse of the tremendous sociological importance that it has had through the ages. This has necessitated the building of new language values for it[3]—and until this task has been accomplished there is certainly a compelling invitation to giving it unbridled freedom in its own right.[4]

In this book I have attempted to keep away from the pathological, but failure to develop true heterosexual maturity is so common that it is perhaps pardonable to discuss immaturity—if, indeed, its prevalence allows it to be considered as abnormal or pathological. The adolescent expresses the sexual urge in all sorts of unusual ways[5] because our culture bans heterosexual intimacy outside of marriage. It is only as the heterosexual drive really ripens or fails to ripen that we find out whether the so-called "perversions" (which run the whole gamut of acts that can excite the genital area) are of value in themselves or are merely substitutes for a heterosexual expression that will take place as soon as our culture allows it. Some clues are given in the phantasy life that accompanies the acts. However, the matter is not so simple as might appear, since various social factors (of which the most notorious is the upsetting of the sex ratio in urbanization)[6]

1 See Chapter 18.

2 *Trends*, pp. 414–423. The rapidly increasing number of places (e.g., filling stations) where contraceptives may be purchased might be taken as some measure of this.

3 Chapter 10.   4 Chapter 9.

5 Chapter 10, pp. 134 f.   6 *Trends*, pp. 467–468.

sometimes prevent fulfillment of the heterosexual drive even if it has developed quite normally.

While this heterosexual stage does not begin to show itself until midway through adolescence, certain of its conditioning factors go back to infancy and early childhood, when the child first becomes aware of the patterns of heterosexual relationship. The social trends are of importance here—those in parent education as to the part their own lives play in the choices which their children make.[7] There are two quite distinct sets of patterns which the child gets from these early years.

The first is the need to carry out in marriage the unresolved Oedipus complex.[8] The second is the need to duplicate or avoid certain characteristics of the parent of opposite sex. So courtesy, dominance, gentleness, honesty, and what not are traits zealously sought or shunned as the child begins to reach out towards his own marriage. Whatever the circumstances, one frequently sees a boy or a girl apparently interested in only one type of partner. This may have many contributing factors (and is certainly subject to trends in the roaming range of children), but these must include the patterns the child has seen in his own family.

Early in adolescence (at eleven or twelve) there develops a "negative" phase in which both boys and girls show a shy fear of the other sex—often coupled with loud overcompensating announcements of dislike or indifference. How much of this represents a continuation in the heterosexual field of the problems of narcissism and homosexuality discussed in the two previous chapters, and how much represents alarm at the drive that is soon to appear, I don't know. Part of this particular aspect of the problem is tied up with the difference in the rate of maturation of the

[7] *Trends*, pp. 792 ff.   [8] Healy, pp. 158 ff.

two sexes—though this doesn't show itself in dramatic form until around fourteen. Although girls mature much more rapidly than boys, there has been no recognition of this on the part of our institutional structure.[9]

As adolescence advances and the problem of heterosexuality definitely emerges for the child, there is need to "feel" for the new relationships on the basis of the old.[10] This involves a restatement of practically all the problems of this book in terms of "what my family will be like"[11] instead of "what my family has been." The tensions that this sets up for the envelope can either be imagined or observed (if one has contact with the lightning-like inconsistencies of the usual adolescent). Of the greatest importance here are trends in the ease with which class lines are crossed and rigid social classifications are broken.[12] While this particular phase of the problem has to do with all the personal and social aspects of the child's life, perhaps the most poignant conflict (if we are to believe the testimony of the arts) occurs in the child's re-evaluation of his background.[13] This often demands of him the bitterest denunciation of everything that has been dearest. And no less disturbing is his sudden feeling of shame over various quite minor traits and characteristics in his parents or "people." In attempting to ease the conflict between Old World and New World standards for these adolescents it has

[9] However, see Prescott, pp. 248–249.

[10] There are many clear pictures of this in the case histories of Peter Blos, *The Adolescent Personality* (New York, Appleton-Century, 1941); note particularly pp. 248 ff.

[11] The fact that persons indentify with what they expect to be rather than what they are is used statistically by P. F. Lazarsfeld and others in their study of voting, *The People's Choice* (New York, Duell, 1944); note particularly pp. 20 ff.

[12] I have never run across any statistical assay of this important matter,—but such books, for instance, as *Middletown in Transition*, by R. S. and Helen Lynd (New York, Harcourt, 1937) are full of indications that class lines are becoming more rigid and hard to cross.

[13] That we teach each child that class lines can and should be crossed though the facts are definitely of the opposite trend, doesn't add to one's comfort.

often been forgotten that whatever the parents are or have the child must reject. It is even possible that this particular conflict over cultural patterns and standards drains off a fire of rebellion and re-evaluation that would be far more devastating if it had to express itself on personal rather than social levels.

A second consideration in this feeling for new relationships has to do with the "trying out" of new affectional ties which do not carry responsibility. As already stated, these sometimes represent strong attachments to persons of the same sex or older persons of the opposite sex.[14] A serious complication in this period of tentative approaches is presented by the fact that heterosexual experiences offer returns of the richest and most intense value.[15] All trends in the social taboo of such relationships are important. As to what the child "does about it," the most interesting (and probably the most widespread) are the developments of various sublimations in poetry, art, athletics, and so forth. Theoretically there should be a high correlation in any society between the extent of social taboo on physical relationships between the sexes and the development of the sublimative activities.[16] However, one must not forget that in these years of late adolescence for the normal person there is no immediate emotional substitute for the sexual act.

This is as far as my data go with any sort of completeness. Even with sharp changes in trends in the age of marriage[17] or in trends in social sanction of marriage supported by the parents of one or both parties,[18] this important step takes place much later than the age at which we see all but a few of our patients.

[14] Chapter 18.   [15] Chapter 9.
[16] The variables are so hard to define that the degree of correlation would probably turn out to be about what the research student had hoped for.
[17] *Trends*, pp. 303, 680.
[18] Until 1935 I did not know of a single marriage which was being supported by parents without "excuse" or "explanation." In the last dozen years this has become a frequent experience. The reader will remember that I am less interested in the

One of the problems of marriage, however, we do see forming before the age limit of our work. This is what the child wants to see in the opposite sex. (And there is no area in which the envelope more assiduously sieves and remakes all of the material which comes to it.) That is, John does not go with Mary, he does not propose to Mary, nor marry Mary—but rather what he thinks Mary is, what he wants Mary to be. And she has the same attitude towards John. In these days, when we would have tolerance in racial and national relationships, it might be well to realize that it should begin at home. Until in each husband-wife relationship, and then in each parent-child relationship, there can be an acceptance of persons for what they really are instead of for what we want them to be—until then it seems rather footless to the psychiatrist to talk of tolerance in broader sweeps.

fact of such support than in the presence or absence of a feeling that "it isn't quite the right thing to do."

CHAPTER 20

Sibling Rivalry

W_e see children who have the problem of rivalry with other members of their family—chiefly siblings. There are three distinct levels at which this conflict is carried through. On the first is the early struggle with brother and sister in the child's search for belongingness.[1] On the second is the somewhat later struggle with siblings in the field of adequacy,[2] which is in part a carry-over from the earlier struggle and in part a training school for the competition of adult life. On the third level is the struggle with the parent of the same sex for the love of the parent of the opposite sex, in which security issues are also involved.

That the problem is of long standing is attested by the legend of Cain and Abel. Its present prevalence and sharpness bring a steady stream of patients to the psychiatrist, who never ceases to be amazed at the extent of their disturbance over the bitterness of their emotions. Perhaps the very depth of such jealousy makes it necessary for each one to hide it behind a heavy screen of family loyalty and devotion; perhaps the importance of security[3] is so great that few can afford to contemplate anything that threatens it. Be that as it may, none of the other dynamic concepts considered in this book seems to produce in the patient such fresh and acute surprise.

In the early struggle for belongingness, the child gives many indications of keen rivalry long before he knows that he is jealous. The parents, however, are very well aware of the emerging conflict, and fairly early in life they manage to make the child

[1] Chapter 1. [2] Chapter 14.
[3] Chapter 1.

aware of their own disturbance over his unwelcome behavior. I suspect that the problem which appears in this indirect way lasts through life—though subtly hiding itself behind ever more charming garments. But its shiny newness is always there. What starts as open physical violence between brothers and sisters ends up in sly eyeing of the relative successes of each other's grand-children.

The problem of sibling rivalry first appears in those early days when the infant begins to be aware of siblings who demand attention and to devise means of keeping his mother to himself. We tend to forget this for two reasons. All babies obtain so much attention, that we are apt to think of sibling rivalry as appearing only when the arrival of the next youngster dethrones the last. Furthermore, the forces that the infant mobilizes are not very efficient or persistent and hence not particularly bothersome to adults. It is difficult to determine to what extent his protests represent desire of possession of his mother and to what extent determination that no one else shall have her. Both factors are probably present.

The problem becomes sharper of course when the child is faced with acceptance of a younger brother or sister. Often the rivalry picture begins considerably before the actual arrival of the new baby—in fact, as soon as the child realizes that the parents have a new interest.[4] Though, as children differ in their reactions in accordance with their age, we are interested in trends in the spacing of pregnancies[5] and also in trends in parent education in preparing children for the arrival of siblings.[6]

[4] This is often the source of considerable clinical confusion. Parents will frequently entirely miss the point of what are patently sibling-rivalry syndromes because the symptoms so long preceded the actual appearance of the new arrival.
[5] Mildred Parten, "A Statistical Analysis of the Modern Family," *Annals of the American Academy of Political and Social Science*, vol. 160, pp. 29–37, particularly p. 34, March 1932.
[6] *Trends*, pp. 792–794; White House Conference, pp. 147–150.

Regressive behavior is the most common form of reaction. There are a number of reasons for this. The child sees that it is the babyhood of the new arrival which captures the attention of his parents—and therefore what could be more natural than to feel that he too will get attention by returning to infantile ways? So baby talk, bed-wetting, demands for this or that, predominate. Such phenomena can also be explained by the concept of the load.[7] If the arrival of a new baby represents an emotional load for the child, then we should expect responses in the most recently established reflexes—namely, those of speech or sphincter control. To this picture must be added the small child's confusion as to the relationship of the parents to the baby and their relationship to him. This confusion of belongingness[8] and dependence[9] may last through life or gradually clear up if the individual grows up emotionally.

The child also shows a certain amount of aggression towards the new arrival. It seems certain that as the parent (let us say the mother, as she is usually the one more intimately involved) begins to give him less time, he feels resentment over her withdrawal. It is difficult to determine, however, to what extent this resentment becomes a drive against baby as the cause of the mother's withdrawal. As this is a very important point in the matter of the development of the sense of guilt, we are interested in all trends towards educating parents as to the naturalness of sibling rivalry and the mechanisms of jealousy.[10] He may attempt to hurt the baby in various ways or he may shower him with solicitude and affection. The latter type of behavior is frequently taken to be the child's atonement for his jealousy, but more frequently his reasoning is: "My mother gives me less in-

[7] See Chapter 23, pp. 249, 254.   [8] Chapter 1.
[9] Chapter 16.
[10] J. C. Foster and M. L. Mattson, *Nursery School Education* (New York, Appleton-Century, 1939), Chapter XVIII.

terest, she gives the baby more. If I am good to the baby, she will
like me better (give me more time and interest)."

It is not an easy matter to trace the sense of guilt to its source
—to discover how the various rivulets coalesce to make the stream
or just when this occurs. By three or four, however, the child begins to give evidence of rudimentary, diffuse, and poorly verbalized feelings of guilt. But at this age much depends on the relationship between the parents and the new baby. If the latter happens to be just what they were "looking for" as to sex, cuteness,
or some other quality, the problem will be sharpened for the
older child. That is, children can be much disturbed when something is taken away from them—and "righteously" so—without
realizing (or at any rate verbalizing) that the baby is responsible
for their loss, and therefore beginning to hate the baby and to
feel guilty over their hatred. Feelings of guilt do occur in sibling
rivalry, but it is important to recognize that, long before they
spontaneously arise, parents suppose them to be there (as they
see the child's resentment against the withdrawal of their interest and project their own feelings of guilt). Perhaps one sees this
best in the case of severely handicapped children. Even before
the next pregnancy the parents of such a child may begin to
wonder "whether it will be fair to him" and are sensitized to a
show of jealousy. The earliest disturbance on the child's part is
so interpreted—first, because they have been expecting it, and,
second, because they project in this way their own feelings of
guilt over conspiring to bring to the scene a rival who will so
easily become complete master of the situation.[11]

As the child begins to attend school—at about the age of five—
the problem of rivalry acquires new aspects, to which he may re-

[11] Sometimes, of course, their hesitancy in having another child comes from an
understandable fear of visiting a handicap upon the next arrival as well as from
these feelings of guilt.

act in several ways.[12] (1) This dramatic crystallization of the push-ing-out process may suddenly increase his appreciation of the favored position of the younger child. To establish his depend-ence, he may resort to baby talk, bed-wetting, thumb-sucking, or even stubborn refusal to go to school, with perhaps nausea and vomiting. (2) On the other hand the impact of school life may lead to identification with older children. When the child recog-nizes the rivalry thus involved, his behavior pattern is much more allied to that of adequacy[13] than that of security.[14] (3) Some-times it is at this point that the problem of the middle child be-comes apparent. Though many children have this status before the age of five, they still tend to capitalize on babyhood charac-teristics even if they have younger siblings. These middle chil-dren don't have the prestige of the oldest or the dependence of the youngest. At school age their patterns are likely to be of the attention-getting, pushing sort. Various trends have a bearing on all three rivalry situations—those in the age at which children join preschool groups or go to school,[15] those in spacing children for economic, psychological, and biological reasons, and those in the size of the family.[16]

By seven or eight the child has definitely entered the struggle for adequacy and in general can imagine himself as having the same problems as all others who have grown beyond the depend-ency stage. If we take a long enough view of the trends of the age of dependency, we see that the period has gradually lengthened. How this first occurred we don't know, but comparatively recent extension of the span of school attendance and delay in the age of employment have been contributing factors.[17] (1) The child

12 White House Conference, pp. 153–156. Particularly note the rapid increase in preschool groups in the last six years.
13 Chapter 14.
14 Chapter 1.
15 White House Conference, pp. 153–156.
16 *Trends,* pp. 683–684.
17 *Trends,* pp. 303, 342.

recognizes his rivalry with the parent of the same sex to the point where he can verbalize it. He now makes all sorts of efforts at punishing, shaming, and making trouble for this parent. His elders have recognized earlier signs of jealousy, of course, but these were not on the conscious level.[18] (2) The child's identification with older children is much more complete, and he feels much more on even terms with them. Thus muscular or verbal struggles for power replace the earlier regressive tendencies in his behavior pattern. (3) We now see, fully flowering, the working out of a useful mechanism—the struggle between siblings as a preparation for the later struggle with one's peers. The child has no picture of the future use of these tricks, but he nevertheless consciously tries out various modes of attack and defense. One sees this in discussing family fights with children. They would not know how to get along without fighting. "It's fun," they say. How often the harassed parent sees the children tentatively reaching out in this or that direction until a fight can be started. The child derives some of his satisfaction from the defeat of a sibling but most of it from the adventure of combat.

By eight the child has pretty thoroughly incorporated the sense of guilt into his own personality structure, so that—regardless of its origin—he now has the feeling that he himself is pointing the finger of accusation. His behavior patterns do not change —he may still attempt bitter punishment of the baby or show sweet solicitude for him. But in the latter case he is more consciously motivated by self-imposed atonement. As the sense of guilt is the type of problem with which the educator more and more feels he must help the child,[19] we are interested in educational trends as to the naturalness of sibling rivalry.

Because of the child's increased vulnerability during adoles-

[18] For the psychoanalytic formulation of the Oedipus complex, see Healy, pp. 128 ff.

[19] Foster and Mattson, *op. cit.*

cence, all the drives coming from the sense of guilt sweep merci-
lessly over him, and all the issues of the struggle with the environment are brought more sharply into focus. Every petty matter
is enlarged, and the passing difficulties of the earlier period now
assume gigantic proportions.[20] We are therefore interested in all
trends affecting the length of this period.[21] We are also interested
in trends in the restriction of immigration, since the conflict between Old and New World patterns is intensified at this time.[22]
The problem of rivalry with parents becomes entangled with
that of the drive for independence,[23] and the shame for parents
which is a natural part of the latter problem strengthens the
rivalry issue.

In the preceding pages I have said nothing as to the rivalry
patterns existing between husband and wife—though this in
itself would seem to be a logical working forward of the struggle
of childhood—expressing itself in both the security and adequacy
areas. This is a matter that I hesitate to deal with directly because
it stretches beyond the years for which I have reliable data. However, we must remember that serious problems arise for the child
as parents feverishly attempt to outbid each other for his affection.[24] This is true for the calculating youngster who shrewdly
plays one parent against the other—forever free from discipline.
And it is equally true for the confused novitiate at life who finds
himself exposed to pressing bids for attention.

[20] This is well shown all through Peter Blos, *The Adolescent Personality* (New
York, Appleton-Century, 1941).

[21] *Trends*, p. 303.

[22] *Trends*, p. 52. The psychiatrist working in an area where there are very large
numbers of first- and second-generation foreign-born wonders what heavy new personal loads will appear when the convenient scapegoat of Old and New World
standards has disappeared.

[23] Chapter 16.

[24] See J. S. Plant, "The Psychiatrist Views Children of Divorced Parents" in *Law
and Contemporary Problems: Children of Divorced Parents* (Durham, Duke University School of Law, 1944), vol. 10, no. 5, pp. 807–818.

CHAPTER 21

Personality Differences

We see children who wonder "how they got this way." This is an assay, by the individual, of the result of the developments of all the problems previously considered in this book plus, perhaps, certain inherited patterns or trends. We may see various threads interweaving, but to the child it is only the general resulting pattern that is important. There exist so many excellent theories, supported by so many excellent scholars, that it comes as somewhat of a shock that the child looks upon his personality as a relatively simple and fixed affair. With fresh naïveté he simply announces himself as "this or that sort of person." Not that this makes the problem less important to him—so often the child comes to us wishing to be "a different sort of person" rather than merely wanting to clear up some specific difficulty!

I have spent considerable time wondering whether this particular preoccupation of patients should be raised to the importance of a problem. It unquestionably has that value to the child. Discussions of unpopularity, bossiness, pliability, warmth, or gaiety may fill our ponderous tomes, but such qualities are simple entities to our patients. Well, this is not entirely so. To the extent that the individual sees his peculiarities as measured against what others show, and to the extent that he is interested in the difference between his trait and the standard, rather than just in his trait, we approach the problem of individual difference.[1] Also, certain traits are placed under stress by the cultural pattern or are changed by it, and he feels this stress or change. But at least on the verbal level these are not the child's worries. He gives simple, clear accounts of his oddities with something of the

[1] Chapter 4.

straightforward pride of an owner pointing out the idioms of his house. A comparison is obviously implied, but the simple fact of the presence of the trait seems, at the moment, to be all that matters.

However, our patients are not alone in this naïveté. Certainly there is a long line of distinguished authorities who have had the feeling that, in some way, certain personality patterns are quite as predetermined and fixed as certain physical characteristics. For instance, we hear of psychopathic personalities.[2] Kretschmer[3] attempted to tie in the matter of fairly well-defined personality types to body build, and there is an interesting new attempt along something of the same line by Sheldon.[4] As one works with children, he gets more and more the feeling that all the day-by-day changes fit into a structure that is congenitally patterned. Admittedly, this cannot as yet be proved. But be that as it may, the problem is a very real one to children—especially during the stormy and vulnerable period of adolescence. What it is before that period is hard to determine. Children under twelve tell me that they do such and such things or feel in such and such a way —but it is rarely that they tell me that they are such and such. When such a child (that is, under twelve) does speak of himself as such and such a person, it has been my experience that he is repeating something he has been *told*. He is perfectly willing to use his selfishness, his shyness, or his appealing character as an excuse for the various things he does. He doesn't seem to have the feeling that he "will always be this way"—or that this is really himself.

By eleven or twelve there is a beginning realization that he has

[2] D. K. Henderson, *Psychopathic States* (New York Academy of Medicine, Salmon Committee for Psychiatry and Mental Hygiene, Thomas W. Salmon Memorial Lectures) (New York, Norton, 1939); William Healy and others, *Reconstructing Behavior in Youth* (New York, Knopf, 1929), p. 70.

[3] Ernst Kretschmer, *Physique and Character* (New York, Harcourt, 1925).

[4] W. H. Sheldon and S. S. Stevens, *The Varieties of Temperament* (New York, Harper, 1942).

such and such traits ("I am shy" or "I am slow"). Perhaps this change is due only to the fact that in every aspect of life the child now sees himself more clearly as an individual. Anyway, he now rides the trait more certainly; he is more definitely depressed than before if it is a "bad" one or more certainly happy about the future if it is a socially acceptable one. The youngster is quite as much at sea as to the origin of these traits as we are. In breezy fashion he usually has one of three answers. (1) Heredity—"I am just like my mother." This is perhaps no more than a relic of the earlier period mentioned in the last section. Certainly most children have been described in such fashion all through the first ten years. (2) Identification—the youngster says that he is like some person he has known, without seeming to have to make a connection. (3) Experience—"I have always been lame, and so I am self-conscious."

It is around fourteen or fifteen that there begins to be insistent, and often anxious, questioning as to how he "got this way." This is so much tied up with the whole problem of narcissism[5] that it is difficult to separate the two. The need to feel different[6] also interweaves here, though certainly not so intimately. This close relationship to the problem of narcissism means that there is now not only recognition of the trait but minute appraisal of it. The child's reaction tends to take the form of either a panicky, grotesque effort at hiding the picture from others or a dismal and unconsolable acceptance—with the blackest picture of the future.

It is of course possible that narcissism is not at the bottom of these anxious assays. Perhaps the obverse is the more correct view—that these personality pictures do begin to take shape as compelling entities at this time and so provide a mainspring for the development of narcissism. Or it may be that during adolescence, certain quite definite physical characteristics begin to assert themselves in compelling fashion. These may be forcing the

[5] Chapter 17.   [6] Chapter 4.

child to realize for the first time that he belongs outside the average range. I see these developments most commonly in: (1) Youngsters who show very shallow emotional reactions[7] and who now seem to realize this inadequacy. There is a hurried, intense effort at self-justification. One gets the *feeling* that such youngsters first recognize their difference from others at this age period. (2) Children who are "fine" in the sensitive sense—who lack a sort of emotional toughness. Once more, it is my own experience that it is in the middle teens that the child recognizes himself as a person of this type. Admittedly, he has been seen as such by others for years, and at those earlier times has often said that he is described as such. (3) Children who have to a high degree the characteristics of the opposite sex. Here, again, the effeminate boy and the masculine girl seem to have the matter sharply accentuated for them at this time.

As the child approaches sixteen he begins to build his life pattern around certain peculiarities he has noted. Here it is our experience that he follows one of three fairly definite patterns. (1) He may continue one of the two ways of reacting that are described in the previous section. (2) There may be a studied and persistent effort at changing the particular trait that has been disturbing to him. (3) He may make various efforts towards a life adjustment that will make the trait a bearable one. For instance, if he feels himself unusually shy he may prepare for some form of research work where he very probably will not have to meet many people.

[7] This is the group described by D. K. Henderson, *op. cit.* It must be obvious that my own formulation presupposes a physical basis (some sort of defect in the development of the visceral nervous system) for the psychopathic personality. I hold to this where there is a rigid description of the type that Henderson employs; obviously I do not hold to it where "psychopathic personality" is used as a catchall term for anything that we cannot otherwise define.

CHAPTER 22

Some Other Problems

We speak of a "problem" whenever a large number of bits of behavior seem to show a certain fairly constant core or whenever we find a pattern repeated fairly often in the arc stimulus-response.[1] With the definition used in this book there is no fixed number to be found. Therefore, as has already been conceded, in time many of the twenty-one discussed in the preceding chapters may be seen to be rationalizations rather than problems, and it is just as likely that many more than twenty-one will be formulated.

Some of these are tentatively listed below. I have not attempted to set them out in chronological sequence because I have run into them much less frequently and usually with much less insistence on the child's part as to their continuing importance. Though to many children they have a quite unitary completeness-in-themselves, as they talked about them I missed the element of growth—the orderly progression of changes seen in the other problems appeared to be lacking here. As the result of different experience, other workers may feel that some or all of the additions deserve to be dealt with as full-blown problems.

1. GOALS AND IDEALS. Do they come from identifications? Is their essential parochialism of value? And of how much value? Are they inductive or deductive phenomena? The task of commingling personal goals with the goals of the group in such a way that they are not lost, as the true artistry of life. The relationship of growth and decay to shifting goals. The whole concept of goals (both social and personal) as changing with cultural patterns.

[1] A "need" in Murray's sense. See Appendix, p. 263.

2. SUCCESS. What is it—situations, large or small, where "nobody else would do"? What kinds of personality need fame (an impersonalized or symbolized success)? The mechanism by which notoriety becomes success—experiences that lead one to be satisfied if he can hold the center of the stage. Masochism and success —why are martyrs happy?

3. SUICIDE. Why do people go on living? What is the relationship between the dictum that all suicides are mentally deranged and the obvious fact that suicide represents the most logical thing one can do? Why are the rates so fixed despite the fact that suicide is perhaps the most personal and intimate of all human phenomena? What is the relationship of suicide to style and custom? Why do so few children (who have excessive phantasies on the matter) commit suicide? Since suicide is a great human crisis, why is its literature (collections of final notes left by suicides) so poverty-stricken and unrevealing?

4. SENSE OF HUMOR. What is it? Can it be developed? Why do we consider that the choicest and most devastating way to damn a person is to say that he has no sense of humor? Why do some individuals invite teasing and can this be overcome? Is it related to lack of objectivity? Is the sense of humor entirely unrelated to intelligence? Slapstick, punning, practical joking, and dry wit in relation to personality types.

5. IMMORTALITY. Why do people believe in it? When can people afford to give up this belief—and under what conditions do they return to it? Can individuals ever conceive of death—of something they have never experienced? To what extent do our own failures demand "another chance"—either in our own lives or those of our children?

6. INSANITY. Is this a discrete phenomenon or a set of attitudes (a way of solving the problem of life) that shades imperceptibly off from sanity? What is the effect of heredity and environment?

Why doesn't insanity develop in childhood? Or are all children insane, particularly adolescents?

7. THE UNCONSCIOUS. What is its nature and what part does it play in our conscious life? How far does it dominate and how insistent are its demands through dreams, slips of the tongue, etc.?

CHAPTER 23

The Meaning of Meaning

The clinical data of the preceding pages invite—demand—the setting up of certain constructs. They were collected in terms of constructs of course, but the latter were tentative at first and were often changed. Those outlined below are not final either and undoubtedly will also be changed—perhaps given up. However, it is my responsibility to delineate what, at this date and with these data, seem to be the sensible and demanded theoretical formulations that further knowledge must test. This theory should fit the formulations that I have earlier attempted.

THE QUESTION OF MEANING

In *Personality and the Cultural Pattern* the word "meaning" appears probably more frequently than any other key word. The reader is constantly reminded that everything must be thought of in terms of what it means to the individual. The building stones of an individual-centered world are fashioned by their meaning to the individual. But what is the meaning of "meaning"? It is this question to which the present book, as I see it, has been addressed, and I hope that it achieves something more than a mere substitution of words.

We can now think of the meaning of a phenomenon as its relationship to the series of problems that the individual is working out. The war came to John Smith. As a young adult he was already attempting to find some satisfactory balance between his affectional ties, his economic needs, his desire for adventure and the new, his need for prestige, and an earlier deep-seated competition with a brother—to mention but a few of the dynamic, de-

veloping problems that preoccupied him.[1] Each of these many
problems had jostled each day, but this very movement had
tended towards a livable balance—a *modus vivendi* that we call
"adjustment." The problem introduced by the war changed the
values and outlooks of each of the old ones. But it did more than
that—these same new values tugged away at the tenacity and
inertia (memories, identifications, etc.) of each of the old relationships. Thus endless perturbations occurred in John Smith.
If we could describe them all in terms of the progress of each of
his problems, we should properly know what this war "meant" to
this John Smith. But complicated as the situation is—there is
more, in the sense that John has a projective mechanism that
gives him an advance picture (biased by his own needs) of how
his total situation will be affected. Furthermore, the relative
weights of events such as war and of his picture of them will differ from moment to moment.

Therefore no exposition of "meaning" can even attempt to be
complete. What has been done in this book is never more than a
statement of "the way the thing works." In setting out a series of
continuing problems, in giving some conception of the delicacy
of their balance, and interbalance, one only opens vistas. Nevertheless, though every item in the previous pages is tentative, I
do have faith in the total structure as an exposition of the way in
which the problem of meaning can be attacked.

THE DEVELOPMENT OF THE PROBLEMS

I have set out some twenty-one problems with which the personality deals in its dynamic, ever-shifting efforts to relieve certain tensions. It is the development of these problems from min-

---

[1] An analogy, fairly complex but still too simple, exists in a beaker of water
containing—in solution—five different chemical compounds. Each of these inter-
changes with the other until a fair state of stability is attained. If now a sixth com-
pound is introduced, the character of the water is changed, there is a stability to
be attained between each of the five and the sixth, and a new relationship is set
up between each of the original five.

ute to minute that gives the meaning of any new phenomenon, defines what the envelope will transmit and to what extent the psycho-osmotic reactions will distort the material as it passes, and determines the readiness of the individual for any new experience.

Each problem has been dealt with in a separate chapter. Following a definition of the issues involved, its development has been traced through the years of childhood. The explanation for this rather brash dating has already been given in the Introduction, but two points demand emphasis here. The first point is that the reader should not go through the book to discover "what problems or symptoms a thirty-seven-month-old child should have." The reason for the first point is imbedded in this second—namely, that the material is presented on a basis entirely different from that upon which it was collected. The problems, as problems, were abstracted from the clinical scene. For certain practical reasons they have been re-stated since their formulation on a chronological basis. In other words, the problems are the product of many particular (in a personal sense) cases, and in this book they have again been particularized (in a temporal sense).

Presented in this way, certain of the twenty-one problems bulk large in the early years, while others seem to put in a later appearance—and certainly so for their moment of greatest activity and "importance." This has a direct relationship to my earlier discussion of the structure of the personality.[2] There I roughly set off three areas of the personality. (1) The part with which we are born. In terms of the present book this might be defined as the "potentiality of having these twenty-one problems." (2) The part that comprises the mental habits or attitudes of the individual—a part that cannot be rigidly separated from the third part. Here I placed those matters concerning which a reaction pattern is established at a fairly early period, from then on mov-

2 Plant, pp. 73–91.

ing within a relatively narrow range. The reader will find the three problems earlier assigned to the second part of the personality[3] appearing once more in this book[4] and differing from the other eighteen only in that they seem to make an earlier appearance and in their demand that the individual make some sort of habitual adjustment to them. (3) The part that is lightly termed "the rest of the personality."[5] This roughly comprises at least the other eighteen problems of the present book.

It may well mystify that I have made a distinction between the second and third parts, when it would now appear that quite similar questions and mechanisms are at work in each. The answer, I think, lies in the fact that the age limit at our clinic is sixteen. It is quite possible that other problems besides security, authority, and temperamental adjustment to reality require a habitual type of adjustment, but they are ones which arise in serious form at a later period than that covered in the present book. Consequently a student of a later age group might be inclined to synchronize parts two and three. But if no distinction were made here, the description of the personality of a very young infant would include all twenty-one problems.[6]

As briefly stated in the Introduction, though all twenty-one problems appear at the clinic with such frequency as to demand that we call them "common," each one was not observed in every child. There are four possible reasons for this. (1) Perhaps these problems are by no means universal. (2) Perhaps I wasn't looking for all of them in any particular instance. (3) Perhaps at the time I was working with a certain child one or another problem was in "perfect balance."[7] (4) Perhaps at the time I was working with

[3] See Plant, pp. 83–88. [4] That is, those in Chapters 1, 2, and 11.
[5] Plant, pp. 88–91. [6] Plant, pp. 88 ff.
[7] Of course, as long as there is some question whether these problems exist and as long as I don't know whether, even if they exist, they ever settle into a perfect balance, this doesn't constitute a very plausible reason. However, I have assumed that there may be times when the answer the child wants and the answer presented by the environment are nearly enough equated to mean that there is prac-

the child certain problems were so pressing that the others were simply crowded out of consideration—even though there and actually operating.

THREE COROLLARIES

In conclusion three corollaries of my theoretical formulations should also be stated.

(1) The first[8] is that we don't adjust problems so much as we adjust to having problems. In my previous book there is the implication that some problems (notably those in the areas of security, authority, and reality) are once and for all cleared up in early life situations. What apparently happens is that in time the patient begins to develop certain habitual modes of reacting to each problem.[9] At first there are wide and frequent fluctuations between satisfaction and thwarting—fluctuations that gradually lessen the length of their arc and finally swing through a very narrow range.

It is this phenomenon that gives the individual the feeling that he has solved the problem. (And well he may have!—if we recognize that it is the unusual and startling that bring problems to the level of awareness.) The reader may remember that in the earlier discussion of the process of "hardening" I spoke of that patterning, or facilitation, of emotional reactions with which we are all familiar. Thus "solving" a problem means that we have learned somehow to handle it because of its relatively narrow and accustomed swings between satisfaction and frustration.[10] Such a view entirely fits in with our recognition of security, authority, and reality as areas in which the earliest adjustments are made.

tically no thwarting or blocking or sublimation involved. I have also assumed that with this sort of balance the problem remains below the threshold of attention.

8 Plant, p. 90.

9 At this stage the appearance of my "problems" is much like that of Murray's "needs" (see Appendix, p. 263).

10 Plant, p. 201. The neurological mechanisms involved differ in the two instances, but in both is involved a tendency towards patterning that becomes familiar by repetition.

It is this fact that leads to our usual feeling that these problems are solved or definitely adjusted by the individual before he goes on to other matters.

One is tempted here to dwell on the importance of this corollary in its implications for the whole therapeutic and manipulative structure of psychiatry. Up to now the aim has been to remove tensions, whereas the present theory would direct therapy towards adjusting the individual to the fact that he has these tensions. On such a basis how should we recognize a "well-adjusted" individual, if by chance we ever saw one? We shouldn't expect a person with an irrevocably found security and a certain fixed degree of so-called extraversion, and so on. Rather the picture would be of one who had accepted the unending quest and venture of life as a livable fact, and who had decreased the arcs of all his problems to such short lengths that he never had to say, "Now I have to come to quits with that all over again."

(2) The second corollary is that we are now interested in what people are trying to do rather than in what they are doing. We see every act as an effort at making an adjustment within a problem. (Will it not be a glorious day when adults generally look upon bothersome children as individuals who are trying to solve problems instead of individuals who are trying to be problems?) Two subsidiary statements under this corollary may be made:

(a) Any specific bit of conduct comes to have very little significance—in itself. Stealing may appear to be about the same phenomenon in fifty different children, but it changes to fifty different phenomena as soon as we think of it as an effort at working out one or another combination of problems. Most of the approaches to conduct disorders have begun with the question "How many causes are there for stealing?" The approach of this book is rather "How many results are there of insecurity?" The usual approach took a socially determined fact (delinquency) and tried to calibrate it in psychological terms (I.Q., personality type, etc.). Mountains of statistics compiled in this way will tell us nothing. But if stealing is seen as one of the many ways in which the child attacks problems of growth and adjustment, such an act immediately becomes a psychologically determined bit of data and can be readily calibrated against any other dynamic psychological phenomena.

(b) While theoretically the twenty-one problems outlined in this book are closely interlocked and are always operating, as a practical matter they have different weights for actual children. One sees this in two ways. Some children are, even for long periods, so preoccupied with working out a solution for one or two problems that it is of no avail to point out to them that in every other sector of life they are far better "adjusted" than most individuals. It is distressing, with such children, to discover what poor results come from pointing out the satisfactions that lie about if they will but turn their attention from the one area they have focused on. Conversely, some children are so comfortable in their adjustment to one or two problems (this in terms of shortening the arcs, as described above) that they appear entirely oblivious to the messes they are making in other fields. These children seem well adjusted—if we can use that term here to describe individuals who show no overt symptoms of unhappiness. But admittedly, if such a child is studied carefully he will show great confusion in regard to many of what one thinks of as important problems of life adjustment. To repeat, these two sorts of experience seem to indicate that, for any given child at any given time, one or another problem has greater weight than the others.

(3) The third corollary concerns the importance of the concept of the "load." This is the sum of the number and severity of the stresses that the child is at the moment experiencing. The stress may come from one particularly knotty problem or from slight difficulty with all the problems (or from any combination between these two). The load itself is of course related specifically

to the problems which give rise to it. But because of the osmotic character of the envelope, the expression of the load is not so much related to the problems themselves as it is to the conditions in the environment which invite expression. It is for this reason that stealing may be the means of expressing the load arising from any one or all of the twenty-one problems in one situation, whereas enuresis may be the means of expressing the load arising from the same problems in another situation. It is in this sense that I so definitely hold that behavior is not specific to the problem which lies behind it.

Such a view is admittedly contrary to the usual psychiatric formulation. It would presume that problems in speech, writing, enuresis, or sexual adjustment ought to be those most frequently met (and this is the case) in the children referred to a guidance clinic. This is not because they are closely linked with the child's commonest problems but because they involve the "highest" and least stable of the reflex mechanisms, so that a load from any source is most likely to show itself here. A frustration (or load) will register itself first of all upon the most sensitive indicator without implying that there is any specific relation between the nature of the disturbance and the nature of the indicator. The sensitivity of the indicator is measured by its complexity and/or our ability to read its changes. This last statement is based on my supposition that many behavior disorders seem to be the only matters to bother about simply because, from our point of view, they are the most unusual phenomena. In our culture, for example, many disturbances would be expressed by sexual phenomena which in another culture would have entirely different manifestations.[11] If a child is referred because of excessive masturbation, my view is that therapy should probably not be primarily directed towards a reduction in the amount of masturba-

[11] Abram Kardiner, *The Individual and His Society*, New York, Columbia University Press, 1939.

tion (a point which many others have already recognized), and further that very little attention should be given to this child's sexual problems (a point which represents a radical departure from most modern psychiatric theory). Rather, he should be assayed for any problem which seemed to be causing serious stress. The reader may recall, as an example, our experience with persistent dirty notes and drawings in school.[12] One does not deny the importance or pervasiveness of sexual problems in pointing out that we have never seen a case of this sort in which the child was properly placed, or happy, in his school work. In other words, though the behavior is sexual in character, the problem is not necessarily so.

THE SOCIAL PRESSURES

It has been my contention that the growth of the personality is constantly affected by social pressures. If we are to develop an individual-centered culture we must first discover the meaning of these pressures in terms of their effect upon the problems the child is trying to work through, and then seek to alleviate the pressures without in some other way contributing to the child's frustration. I certainly do not know the extent to which these social pressures affect all personalities, nor do I know what all these pressures are, but within the framework of the thousands of children I have known it is possible to state that some of them may be.

In the chronological section of each chapter I have made three sets of statements, somewhat interwoven but clearly marked. These relate to (1) the aspect of the problem that the child is beginning to try to work through, (2) the social trends that affect this, and (3) certain typical reactions that the child shows to these trends.[13]

---

[12] Plant, p. 37.
[13] Earlier I had set out these three in parallel columns (which had certain advantages, as it placed relevant material in juxtaposition), but this arrangement proved to be cumbersome.

I have made practically no effort in this book to indicate in what direction a given trend is moving at any given time.[14] As briefly mentioned in the Introduction, there are two reasons for the omission. (1) In many cases, as the reader will find if he goes back to the source material, there have been reversals from period to period. (2) If we are interested in how the thing works rather than in what on any particular date the pressures on the individual are, then the actual direction of the trend at any moment is of little importance. What really matters is that trends exist and have meaning to the child—that these demand interpretation and re-coloring by the envelope as protective measures against pressures whose "meaning" seems inimical. Suppose that the child seeks belongingness from all the members of his immediate household —then the trends in the size of families are important, whether towards larger or smaller. Suppose that the child moves to intel-lectual and emotional maturity at his own rate of cadence—then trends in employment opportunity are important and place cer-tain stresses on him in whichever direction they are moving. Suppose that in relatively strange surroundings the individual has to use material symbols (show of money, automobiles, degrees) as a means of establishing status—then trends in the speed at which populations shift are important.

There are three ways in which a society presses its claims and preoccupations upon the individual:

(1) Through other persons—the most important and continuous

[14] But all those mentioned in the text carry references to reports in which docu-mentary evidence can be found.

The reader may recall my hope (Plant, pp. 53 ff.) that it might be possible to set up ordinates against which varieties of material from a wide series of disciplines could be so measured as to be comparable with each other. I have not achieved that goal, but I feel my presentation moves further in its direction than any other to date. In view of the fact that very much more complete work has already been done in relating the fields of psychology, physiology, and anatomy to pressures affecting the individual, it seemed best to confine the references to trends in the social sciences, though even here the list has not been exhausted. In the main, my object has been to keep the references to a minimum but at the same time to give a gen-eral idea of what the possibilities are.

way. This has been scarcely touched on in the present book because it has been dealt with very extensively in so much other psychiatric writing. My own interest in the two other avenues of pressure lies very largely in the fact that they have been neglected in the literature.

(2) Through secondary developments of steps taken with other ends in view. For instance, during the last forty years there has been a sharp reduction in the number of school buildings in this country. It is fair to assume that this is the result of a desire for efficiency of management, better equipment, a higher grade of teacher, a wider selection of courses, and so forth. It could have been foreseen (and perhaps was) that shifts in the problems of each child would result, but in spite of their importance these were secondary developments. Here, then, are sharp individual stresses at least in the fields of status (Chapter 3), of the feeling of difference (Chapter 4), of cadence (Chapter 6), and of minority race status (Chapter 13), which one might think of as part of the "price that is paid." I have attempted to give a large number of examples of this sort of pressure—partly because it is important and partly because there is so little recognition of it at present in psychiatric literature.

(3) Through purely mechanical changes in the cultural pattern. The reader, I hope, has found at nearly every turn evidence of problems arising out of the fact that steam cannot be efficiently transported—that people have to move to this source of powei. Electricity and chemical sources of energy, on the other hand, are decentralizing—and their development will mean other shifts in social pressures on the individual.

The reader perhaps may feel that most of the trends that have been mentioned interfere with the working out of problems. This is a penalty of psychiatric formulation. A clinic such as ours tends to see only those situations in which there have been thwarting and frustration. Consequently, the whole book would have been badly skewed if it had been an exposition of the interaction of individual and environment. As matters stand, however, the omission of an equal sampling of facilitating social pressures does not seem important. Moreover, it may never be possible to assay or sense pressures that are precisely equal to, and in the same direction as, the development of a problem. In such situations the casual breakdown would not occur—a state of affairs which I have assumed to be the beginning of any fruitful knowlege of or assay of the individual-culture balance.[15]

THE CHILDREN'S REACTIONS

In each chapter I have roughly indicated the general types of reaction with which children respond to environmental pressures. Here, more than anywhere else, it would be disastrous for the therapist to try to match his patient with what the book presents. This is because no two persons have experienced the same tensions. Just as the child sees each social trend in terms of what he can afford, his response to environmental pressures takes the form of a selective, translating process. Thus of two children with precisely the same needs (if that is conceivable), one will develop bed-wetting, the other violent rebellion.

The reactions that children show are therefore dependent upon two quite distinct bases. (1) The child's actual behavior is specific in the sense that it represents an effort on his part to express his response to the pressures that the environment places upon him. (2) But it is also nonspecific in that it is the expression of a "load"[16]—and strikes back at the environment where the environment is most vulnerable or where the child is most unstable. As an example, take enuresis in a given case. It might be seen, as part of the child's effort to compete with the helplessness of a new baby sibling, where the behavior is specific in the sense that it

---

[15] Plant, pp. 45 ff., particularly pp. 58–63.   [16] See pp. 249 f.

copies an act that brings desirable maternal solicitude. It might also be seen in the light of the breakdown of a highly complicated and recently developed mechanism, which would be therefore peculiarly vulnerable under any pressure or load. These two principles underlying behavior are separate, and he is indeed wise who can approximate what fraction of the actual behavior is controlled by each.

To a certain extent, of course, the amount and drive of behavior are influenced by the following: (1) The extent of intrapersonal energy. Thus in situations where an individual is excreting undue amounts of thyroxine or adrenalin he shows, as we should expect, a more aggressive or expressive type of behavior. This also occurs when an individual has more money (so that we see some correlation between inflation and delinquency). (2) The question whether it is the individual's pattern (or that of his group) to work out problems externally or as inner conflicts. The Negro pattern (that is, the pattern of a peasant group) has been very largely one of overt expression of problems. As this group becomes urban, we see many evidences of lower crime and delinquency rates. There also appears to be an increase in neuroses, but one can't be too sure of this last point, because neuroses are still very expensive luxuries and the rise in the number may be in part or entirely due to the fact that the urban Negro now has the money to spend on psychiatric help. Another, perhaps more certainly measured phenomenon is the increase—during recent years—in street fighting, roughing up younger children, and that sort of thing among juveniles. (3) The extent to which the cultural pattern at any time provides for socially acceptable means of sublimating the expression of problems. During the war years, for example, there was a sharp curtailment of school sports and clubs for adolescents, and so a general rise in sexual delinquency shown in our juvenile court statistics was to be expected.

THE FUNCTION OF THE ENVELOPE

To the earlier statements about the envelope some further words should now be added. In our present terms it is the process that stands between the child's development of his needs and the environmental pressures. It is the individual's means of protecting himself from the social trends, or of utilizing them to enrich and work out his goals. Because the envelope is not thought of as a physical entity, the reader is free to use any descriptive allegories that fit his own needs. Thus we could consider it as momentarily changing in thickness or in density or in the rate of its metabolism. There are times when the child's problems are so intense and critical that the envelope effects a complete metamorphosis. In some cases the cultural pressures seem to sweep into the personality to produce complete chaos; in others the child goes blithely on in complete assurance of security despite the fact that he has been bombarded for years with every indication of rejection. And there are many times when the matter lies somewhere between these two extremes.

However, it is not in the envelope itself that material from the environment is given meaning. This comes rather from the individual's adjustment to the twenty-one problems described in the preceding chapters. Yet the envelope has some means of encompassing these problems when it is necessary to fend off unpalatable facts. Thus when I can see "nothing but good" in a person I seem to possess the ability to shut out of consciousness various of his traits and acts and to give new meanings to various others.

In the functional psychoses, the envelope assumes an enormous importance. Against what an impenetrable curtain does the psychiatrist beat! The paranoid can fit every conceivable act into his neat scheme. The depressed seems to be completely deaf to everything that does not deepen his gloom; that the envelope is part of the total central process seems indicated in a statement that one so often hears from patients who have recovered: "It helped that you said those things over and over. I couldn't believe them at the time. But I seemed to want to hear them."

On the other hand, in certain of the organic dysfunctions the envelope seems to be badly shattered—and one thinks particularly of those conditions involving considerable cortical edema. In such cases, the child will show intense fear of persons they call "mother" or "father." That is, there is accurate sensory recognition of the parents but the mechanism which gives them their accustomed meaning is lost, and the child fears them in much the same way that one animal fears the approach of another. I have long been sure that the anesthetist has more than has anyone else to offer us in this matter of the development of meaning. He sees, under highly controlled circumstances, the rapid disappearance of the envelope and its reformation. He can adjust his process to any speed he wishes, and in general he can halt it at any level he wishes. Hypnotism and, indeed, all the phenomena of suggestibility, involve an increased permeability of the envelope.

The word "readiness" is on every educator's lips. "The child will read when he is ready to read."[17] But that the problem of readiness is a problem of meaning—of the envelope—is not as yet recognized. Even those schools that most glibly speak of readiness, consider it a function of maturation. "He will read when he is old enough." By "old enough," we find, is meant the attainment of a certain measurable level (chronological age, intellectual age, etc.). The concepts of this book imply that the child will read (or learn geometry or Latin) when the experience offers him some form of enrichment or growth that is not provided by any other of his experiences. Admittedly a very large fraction of children begin to read at eighty months (or to do algebra at fourteen years). I feel quite sure that the problems of conformity to the group[18]

[17] The psychiatrist hopes for that happy time when the educator will similarly realize that the child will learn algebra or Spanish when he is "ready" for these.

[18] The problems expressed in Chapter 4 (the feeling of difference) and in Chapter 6 (cadence).

are the ones that carry most weight here.[19] Education will not move far in this extremely important problem of readiness until it gives up its preoccupation with maturation and begins to realize that readiness occurs when a certain constellation in the internal development of problems gives some school subject a meaning it did not have before. These things are not easily discovered. We must know (1) what these problems are, (2) how they develop, (3) what meanings their developments give to new material, and (4) the extent to which these meanings affect the permeability of the envelope, before we can be on solid ground in the matter of readiness.

We must remind ourselves that an envelope operates both at the level of intake (between the child's problems and the pressures of the environment) and at the level of outgo (the child's method of reacting to the molding forces about him). It is footless to consider whether in each case it is the same envelope, since we do not give physical properties to the envelope. We say only that the personality acts in a certain way at its periphery. In expressing its various tensions in behavior, it does so at least on the basis of (1) the specific problem being worked out, (2) the recentness of the pattern used in expression (sex, speech, muscular coordination, sphincter control, etc.[20]), (3) certain established ways of reacting that are peculiar to the individual (see Chapter 12), and (4) the sensitivity of the environment to the particular bit of behavior expressed. The first and the last of these conditions ob-

[19] That is, it is most inviting to tie the whole matter of readiness in reading and other academic subjects into the problem of the development of the use of symbols (Chapter 5). This plays its part, of course, but it is my own growing conviction that the problems just mentioned—and others—play even more important rôles.

[20] This hierarchy of reflexes, in which one finds that there is a high correlation between the time at which each reflex matures and its sensitivity to the emotional disturbances of the personality, has not been given adequate recognition in the various theories as to the behavior. The most recently developed reflexes register the individual's disturbance because of their lack of stability. This is not the only reason for the great number of maladjustments in the sexual life of adults—but it has far more importance than has been given it by the psychoanalytic group and others.

viously involve an osmotic process between the personality and the environment. This is well shown in the drive for physical expression of the sexual urge, where, through the envelope, there are myriad forms of actual behavior.

If one accepts this concept of the envelope and its operation, he takes sides immediately in the long-standing fight between the psychologist and sociologist as to whether culture is translated or transmitted by individuals. To the former view this book obviously gives its loyalty.

SUMMATION

Perhaps some of those who have read these pages have looked for what ought to be and what should be done about it. The present book has had nothing to do with either of these questions. My work gives daily evidence of present tragedy, and I have frequently written of my faith in the future—but I am sure that many long years of painstaking study of what is must precede the building of what should be. The reader will do well to forget "good" and "bad"—remembering that so far we do not know whether tension is conducive to growth, and, if so, in what amount and of what duration. It seems likely that a set of conditions in the environment that involves no distortion in the working out of the child's needs (the envelope would disappear because there would be no need for it) is not good for the personality. It also seems likely that a set of conditions in the environment that completely thwarts or distorts the development of those needs (the envelope would disappear through being overwhelmed) is not good for the personality. Between these two extremes we might better admit now our abysmal ignorance.

I have constructed this book with many qualms. These are chiefly due to the false picture of simplicity in its presentation. Yet there seemed to be no other way to set out an orderly assay of a theory that is based on my conception of the problems of behavior as related to the needs of the individual. This approach has been widely spoken of, but there has been no detailed effort at implementing it with an analysis of what these are and how they operate. It seemed to me that, however crude the first product, we must go beyond the easy sweeping stage of "certain biological needs" or "certain basic needs." For those who actually work with children I have tried to provide something of a relatively concrete nature—in full realization of its inadequacies and of the almost grotesque simplicity with which it seems to dress the whole matter. If the reader will not forget that this is "one of the ways in which the whole problem probably can be attacked," he will match the spirit in which the book has been written.

The separation of the whole structure into twenty-one different problems obviously does not fit the life situation, in which these are inextricably interwoven. Furthermore, the division of each problem in terms of its chronological development is highly approximate. Even the order in which particular problems develop may be quite different in different children. Thus, just as in actual life each problem is jostled and thrown off balance by each of the others, each step in the presentation was affected by the previous step.

This summation cannot close without reiteration of the fact that this book does no more than attempt to clarify some of the theory set out in *Personality and the Cultural Pattern*. Primarily it attempts to redefine the word "meaning" so frequently used there. The reader is not to feel that the child is at a certain point "because he has had these experiences" but rather that the child is behaving at this point "as if he had been having these experiences." Thus the whole thing remains as merely an illustration of a way of attacking the problem of behavior.

Appendix

Three other approaches to the central problem of this book are so near to my own that they demand consideration. Furthermore, it gives me a certain sense of security to find that my formulations as a medical practitioner are not in serious conflict with those made by authorities from other disciplines.

PARETO

Pareto in really monumental fashion makes an approach quite similar to the present one.[1] His "residues," of which there are six Classes,[2] are very close to what I term "problems." These residues are arrived at negatively in the sense that they are apparent constants as one strips from a great many bits of behavior those elements which vary from person to person or time to time.[3] At various points he says that the residues are allied to the instincts or sentiments, but he does not define the latter. All Pareto's residues are easily discernible in the problems set out in

---

[1] Vilfredo Pareto, *Mind and Society* (New York, Harcourt, 1935). The original appeared (in Italian, of course) in 1916. It is difficult to read Pareto without starting at the beginning and going right through. In general, Chapters VI, VII, and VIII (pp. 499–884) described the residues. On pages 516–518 appears a usable outline of the six Classes of residues. Chapters IX, X, and XI (pp. 885–1432) deal with derivations—but as these constitute a sort of bridge between residues and derivatives, the reader will also find much about the former here. Chapters XII and XIII (pp. 1433–1914) apply the general theory to the data of history. To the clinician these two chapters seem a bit specious. He who must run may glance at page 516. He who trots will find Volume II enough. For those with more time Volumes II and III will prove rewarding—but all four volumes are worth the effort of the serious student.

[2] The Classes are: (1) instincts for combination—e.g., combinations of similars or opposites; (2) group persistences—persistence of aggregates—e.g., persistence of relations between a person and other persons and places; (III) need for expressing sentiments by external acts—e.g., activity, self-expression; (IV) residues connected with sociality—e.g., pity and cruelty, sacrifice for the good of others; (V) integrity of the individual and his appurtenances—e.g., sentiments of resistance to alterations in the social equilibrium; (VI) the sex residue.

[3] Pareto, *op. cit.*, pp. 481, 499 ff.

the foregoing chapters. That I have attempted to depict twenty-one is perhaps, for the present, no more than a matter of taste. Pareto readily admits[4] that there are others besides those he has described. Some of my problems are completely without representation in his formulations—as, for instance, that of cadence (Chapter 6) because he was not interested in mechanisms that are not projective in character, or that of reaction to failure (Chapter 12) because as a sociologist he had little contact with the kind of clinical material that constantly comes to the psychiatrist. One further point of difference demands statement—Pareto's residues are formulated in terms of "what the mind would like to do," whereas my problems are formulated in terms of "the way the mind acts." In this way my problems are much closer to Murray's[5] needs than to Pareto's residues.

Pareto calls the actual conduct of an individual a "derivative." The rationalization that squares the derivative with the residue he terms a "derivation."[6] The derivations are very largely determined by the insistent demands of the residues—almost as though the latter constantly demanded of the individual an explanation for his conduct. With all his sociology, Pareto understates (as I see it) the extent to which the changing social trends arouse terrific tension in the expression of the residues. My own view is that the derivations are determined as much or more by the changing social scene and its demands as they are by the demands of the residues. It is true that what I have termed the envelope is an osmotic sort of mechanism that is forever protecting the residues from the need for derivations that are too bizarre. But is it not implicit precisely here that there would be little or no need for

[4] Pareto, *op. cit.*, p. 501.   [5] See p. 263.
[6] Pareto, *op. cit.*, p. 508. However, for reasons known only to himself, Pareto later gives up the word "derivative" (the actual conduct). His derivations (rationalizations) are divided into two parts—"the derivation proper and the manifestation to which it leads" (p. 1120). The word "derivative" would seem in many ways quite satisfactory, but the reader is warned that if he actually turns to Pareto he will find instead "manifestation," "theorem," or "pseudo-theorem."

such an envelope if the social pressures were not so very deter-
minative? And is it not a part of our everyday experience that the
envelope frequently does a very imperfect sort of job?[7]

MURRAY

Murray and his co-workers at Harvard[8] have chosen to use the
word "need"—a "need" being arrived at in quite the same manner
as is the residue or problem. If there are many pathways between
a stimulus and a response, these tend to cluster about a rather
definite pattern.[9] Here, once more, is a constant that remains
after variable parts of the total process have been discarded. Murray describes forty-four needs, which he arranges in groups (as
Pareto arranges his residues in classes). However, the Harvard
workers have a much more dynamic view of "need" than Pareto
has of "residue"—it is a sort of habituated pattern of psychological
activity. The reader has found (I hope) my "problem" to be a
concept with "an end in view." About thirty-five of Murray's
needs have this connotation very definitely (e.g., aggression), the
rest not at all (e.g., anxiety).

ANGYAL

Because Angyal[10] has recently made a notable effort at a syn-
thesis of the disciplines that might contribute to a science of the
personality, some statement of comparison should be made. In
the discussion of the psychological functions the following appears: "Symbolism is a triadic constellation, whose terms are: the
primary object, its symbol, and a third member, the subject, for

[7] A piece of work that most beautifully shows the importance of the environment in the development of derivations is Abram Kardiner's *The Individual and
His Society* (New York, Columbia University Press, 1939).

[8] Henry A. Murray and others, *Explorations in Personality* (New York, Oxford
University Press, 1938).

[9] Murray, *op. cit.*, pp. 54–129. Particularly note his definition of "need" (p. 61):
"It is a noun which stands for the fact that a certain trend is apt to recur."

[10] Andras Angyal, *Foundations for a Science of Personality* (New York, Commonwealth Fund, 1941).

whom the symbol *means* the object."[11] Later[12] he elaborates
"means" as existing in terms of the individual's "axiomatic values." This last concept is more allied to Pareto's residues than to
Murray's needs—but in all three concepts (as in my problems)
there is common a nonlogical core that has much persistence.
Angyal has been so anxious to have one think of the personality
and its environment as freely interacting that he has nowhere in
his work a place for what I term the envelope. It seems odd that,
with so clear a concept of a system of values and of the object as
having meaning in terms of that system, he has not adequately
recognized the personality's ability to twist or soften or bend,
heighten or deaden the impact of that object, as it impinges upon
this system of values.

[11] Angyal, *op. cit.*, p. 57.   [12] Angyal, *op. cit.*, p. 166.

References

THE references listed below are cited so frequently in the text as to warrant abbreviation. The rest are given in full in the footnotes. All the authors' names are listed in the Index.

Healy
> William Healy, A. F. Bronner, and A. M. Bowers, *The Structure and Meaning of Psychoanalysis, as Related to Personality and Behavior* (Judge Baker Foundation Publication No. 6). New York, Knopf, 1930.

Plant
> James S. Plant, *Personality and the Cultural Pattern*. New York, Commonwealth Fund, 1937.

Prescott
> Daniel Prescott, *Emotion and the Educative Process,* Report of the Committee on the Relation of Emotion to the Educative Process. Washington, American Council on Education, 1938.

Trends
> *Recent Social Trends in the United States: Report of the President's Research Committee.* New York, McGraw-Hill, 1933.

White House Conference
> White House Conference on Child Health and Protection

References

Called by President Hoover, *White House Conference 1930: Addresses and Abstracts of Committee Reports.* New York, Century [1931].

Young

Kimball Young, *Personality and Problems of Adjustment.* New York, Crofts, 1940.

Index

Culture:
  translation of, by individual, 215, 259
  Western, 92
  See also Individual-centered culture
Curiosity, sex. *See* Sex
Curriculum:
  and adequacy, 176
  and high I.Q., 194
  and lack of interest, 74
  and the teacher, 76
  broadening the base of, 190, 194, 197
  of nursery school in relation to kindergarten, 72
  of primary grades, 21
  word-centered emphasis of, 72

Dancing, 56, 87
Daydreams, 155, 156. *See also* Phantasy
Death:
  and broken family, 38
  and extra-human authority, 39
  and immortality, 241
  and inadequacy, 168
  and insecurity, 22–24
  and religious formulations, 41
  of clan members, 17
Defectives, mental
  and parents' love, 185
  demands adjusted to, 212
  trends in care for, 122–123, 153
Degrees, 252
Delinquency:
  and atypical physical development, 34
  and curtailed activities, 175
  and extra-human authority, 40
  and extraversion, 138

Delinquency *(cont.)*
  and glandular imbalance, 33
  and inflation, 255
  and intellectual retardation, 191
  and social "machinery," 92
  and temporary rejection, 10–11
  and the depression, 97
  and word-centered schools, 73
  as substitute behavior, 35
  calibrated in psychological terms, 248
  decrease, among Negroes, 165, 255
  in broken families, 23–25
  in feeble-minded, 123
  prevention, in New Jersey, 165
  sex, during the war, 87, 255
  upward jump of, in adolescence, 27
  vocational choice and, 108
Dementia praecox:
  and extra-human authority, 41
  beginning of, 145
  dire prognostications of, 143
  early, 144
  See also Psychoses
Dentist, 204
Dependence:
  and adolescence, 37
  and adults in the household, 98
  and "causes," 216
  and growth of self-sufficiency, 90–91
  and handicaps, 98
  and intelligence, 186
  and Old versus New World patterns, 165
  and premature use of symbols, 72
  and sibling rivalry, 233
  as one of the twenty-one problems, *199–209*
  as personality trait, 176
  economic, of women, 121

Education *(cont.)*
    parent, 230–231, 234
    sex, 121, 130–131
    See also College; Kindergarten;
        Nursery school; School; Teacher
Effeminacy:
    and homosexuality in accepted
        sense, 218
    and organic inferiority, 153
    and teasing, 117
    as personality difference, 239
    See also Glands, imbalance of; Sex
"Efficiency mechanism," 63–64
Ego, 46, 50
Egocentricity, 210, 215
Ellis, Havelock, 124, 125, 129
Ellwood, C. A., 17
Emotion:
    difficulty of finding symbols for,
        77
    origin and rôle of, 126, 132, 148–
        149
Emotional development:
    dependence as stage of, *199–209*
    heterosexuality as stage of, *223–
        228*
    homosexuality as stage of, *218–222*
    narcissism as stage of, *210–217*
    See also Maturation; Maturity,
        emotional
Emotional problems:
    and camouflaging symbols, 76
    and reflexes, 150
    and the learning process, 21
    in broken family, 24
    speech disorders and, 31
Emotional quotient, 203
Employment:
    academic prerequisites for, 197
    age of, 37, 233
    and cadence, 252

Employment *(cont.)*
    and minority race status, 164
    delayed, and social responsibility,
        55
    of married women, 12, 96, 201, 204
    war-time, 12, 201
    See also Unemployment
Enuresis:
    and cadence, 79, 83
    and dominating parents, 141
    and first school experience, 19
    and relatives in the household, 16
    and sibling rivalry, 18, 231, 233
    as both specific and nonspecific
        behavior, 254
    as expression of "load," 250
    as sign of dependence, 205
    in war time, 120
    See also Sphincter control
Envelope, the:
    and Angyal's work, 264
    and cadence, 84, 87
    and "causes," 216
    and characteristics of opposite sex,
        117
    and competition, 205
    and dependency relationship, 206
    and emerging homosexuality, 226
    and "meaning," 26
    and narcissism, 211
    and Pareto's residues, 262
    and personal tolerance, 228
    and problems of relationship, 132
    and sex, 121, 123, 131–132, 135
    and shutting out improper ma-
        terial, 106
    and unpopularity, 153
    as distinguished from "wall," 46–
        47
    as interpreter, 23, 252
    as protector, 111, 144

Sexes, the two:
admixture of characteristics in, 111
changing relative importance of, 14
differences in:
and adolescence, 54
and maturation, 86, 124, 144, 225–226
and overt sex behavior, 133–134
and sex language values, 124
and sex taboos, 118
and social cadences, 86
equality of, 124, 198
See also Member rôle
Shallowness, 239
Sheldon, W. H., 139, 140, 237
Shoobs, N. E., 14
Shyness:
and cadence, 86
and school marks, 75
and status preservation, 51
as escape from social authority, 42
as personality trait, 176
as protective device, 153
distinguished from negativism, 47
Sibling rivalry:
and belongingness, 18
and cadence, 83
and early speech difficulties, 72
and enuresis, 254
and failure, 152
and sense of guilt, 61–62
and struggle for adequacy, 173
as one of the twenty-one problems, 229–235
lasting character of, 173–174
three levels of, 229
Siblings, traits of, 18
Sissy, 117, 153. *See also* Effeminacy; Glands, imbalance of

Size. *See* Stature
Skedak, Marie, 181
Skeels, H. M., 181
Sleep, poor, 31, 196
Social class. *See* Class
Social "machinery," 92
Social pressures:
and extraversion, 146
and growth of personality, 251–254
and joining the Church, 216
and left-handedness, 195
and minority race status, 164
and sex, 63
and symbolization, 76
and temperament, 137–139
and the envelope: 262–263
facilitating or interfering, 253–254
for academic rather than vocational training, 190
importance of, 1–2
through secondary developments, 253
toward masturbation, 126
See also Pressures
Social sanction, 227–228. *See also* Authority, social or group
Social sciences, 252
Social status:
and adequacy, 174
and advertising pressure, 86, 178
and failure, 155
and security, 16
and the "wall," 53, 54
attraction to those of lower, 214
college as badge of, 179
determined through competition, 28
early bewilderment over, 15
of Negroes, 165

Stevens, S. S., 139, 140, 237
Stillman, B. W., 196
Strabismus, 175
Strachey, Mrs., 120
Strang, Ruth, 197
Stratification:
  economic and social, 16
  in adolescent behavior, 34
  in school placement, 176
  in type of work, 184
  of pupils on I.Q. basis, 192
  of society on intelligence basis, 197, 198
Street fighting, 255
Stubbornness, 176
Stuttering. *See* Stammering
Sublimation:
  and the cultural pattern, 255
  of sex, 63, 126, 227
Subpersonalities, 102, 104, 107
Substitutive behavior, 85
Suburban living:
  and available playmates, 141, 154
  and possessions, 74, 75
  "wall" thickest in, 53
Success:
  and insecurity, 8, 15
  as problem, 241
  broadening the base of, 135
  masochism and, 241
  symbols and, 74–75, 155
Suggestibility, 257
Suicide, 241
Summer round-ups, 70, 181
Sunday school:
  and different selves, 105
  and extra-human authority, 39
  trends in attendance at, 26
Superego, 104
Swimming pools, 144
Swings. *See* Fluctuations
Symbiosis:
  between sense of guilt and feeling

Symbiosis *(cont.)*
  of difference, 58–59, 63
  in minority-race mechanisms, 158
Symbolization and reality, *68–78*
Symbols:
  and adequacy, 177–178
  and intelligence, 181
  and status preservation, 49, 53
  as efficiency mechanism, 63
  first experience with, 70, 187
  imposed on inadequate experience, 69, 70
  mechanism of unloading on, 177
  necessary to conserve energy, 69
  of being grown up, 55
  of emotional experience, 76–77
  reliance on, for success, 155
  substitution of, for reality, 146
Symptom-complex:
  and disease, 150
  of city worker, 93
  of "unwanted" child, 10
Symptom picture, 85
Symptoms:
  and handedness, 196
  and personality types, 150
  of extraversion and introversion, 144
  of glandular imbalance, 33
  of handicapped children, 98
  of inadequacy, 168, 169
  of insecurity, 14, 151–152, 169
  of overreaching, 83
  of schizophrenia, 110
  of security relationship in gangs, 220
  of sibling rivalry, 230
Syndrome:
  Fröhlich's, 33
  Ganser's, 41
  of insecurity, 13
  of sibling rivalry, 230